The Great

STEAM RA

TIMETABLE

1995

COLIN TYSON

ALAN SUTTON PUBLISHING LIMITED

First published in the United Kingdom in 1995
Alan Sutton Publishing Limited
Phoenix Mill · Far Thrupp · Stroud · Gloucestershire

Copyright © Colin Tyson, 1995

All rights reserved. No part of this publication may be reproduced,
stored in a retrieval system, or transmitted, in any form, or by any
means, electronic, mechanical, photocopying, recording or otherwise,
without the prior permission of the publisher and copyright holder.

British Library Cataloguing in Publication Data

A catalogue record for this book is available from the British Library.

ISBN 0–7509–0909–9

Typesetting by Sonia Desmond
and Alan Sutton Publishing Limited.
Printed in Great Britain by
Ebenezer Baylis, Worcester.

CONTENTS

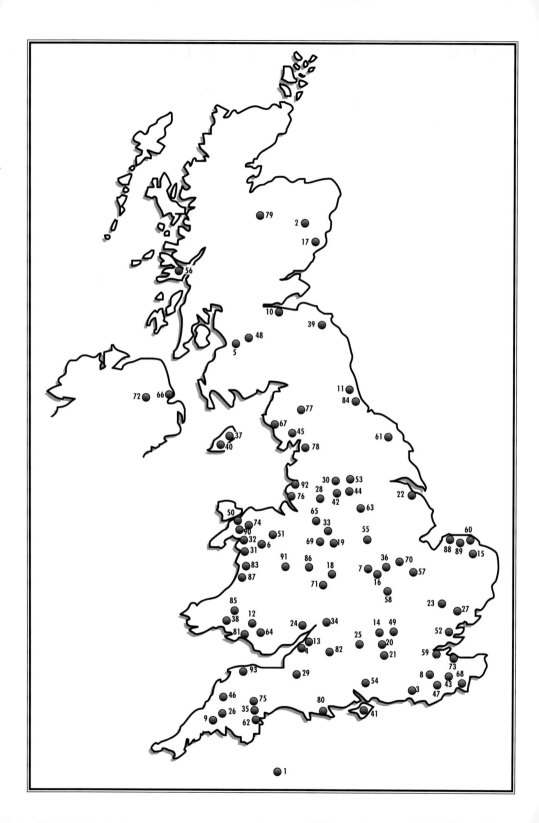

ALPHABETICAL TABLE OF LISTED SITES

1	Alderney Railway	48	Leadhills & Wanlockhead Railway
2	Alford Valley Railway	49	Leighton Buzzard Railway
3	Amberley Chalk Pits Museum	50	Llanberis Lake Railway
4	Avon Valley Railway	51	Llangollen Railway
5	Ayrshire Railway	52	Mangapps Farm Railway
6	Bala Lake Railway	53	Middleton Railway
7	Battlefield Line	54	Mid-Hants Railway
8	Bluebell Railway	55	Midland Railway Centre
9	Bodmin & Wenford Railway	56	Mull & West Highland Railway
10	Bo'ness & Kinneil Railway	57	Nene Valley Railway
11	Bowes Railway	58	Northampton & Lamport Railway
12	Brecon Mountain Railway	59	North Downs Railway
13	Bristol Harbour Railway	60	North Norfolk Railway
14	Buckinghamshire Railway Centre	61	North Yorkshire Moors Railway
15	Bure Valley Railway	62	Paignton & Dartmouth Railway
16	Cadeby Light Railway	63	Peak Rail
17	Caledonian Railway	64	Pontypool & Blaenavon Railway
18	Chasewater Steam Railway	65	Railway Age - Crewe
19	Cheddleton Railway Centre	66	Railway Preservation Society of Ireland
20	Chinnor & Princes Risborough Railway	67	Ravenglass & Eskdale Railway
21	Cholsey & Wallingford Railway	68	Romney, Hythe & Dymchurch Railway
22	Cleethorpes Coast Light Railway	69	Rudyard Lake Railway
23	Colne Valley Railway	70	Rutland Railway Museum
24	Dean Forest Railway	71	Severn Valley Railway
25	Didcot Railway Centre	72	Shanes Castle Railway
26	Dobwalls Railway	73	Sittingbourne & Kemsley Light Railway
27	East Anglian Railway Museum	74	Snowdon Mountain Railway
28	East Lancashire Railway	75	South Devon Railway
29	East Somerset Railway	76	Southport Railway Centre
30	Embsay Steam Railway	77	South Tynedale Railway
31	Fairbourne Railway	78	Steamtown - Carnforth
32	Ffestiniog Railway	79	Strathspey Railway
33	Foxfield Railway	80	Swanage Railway
34	Gloucestershire & Warwickshire Rly	81	Swansea Vale Railway
35	Gorse Blossom Railway	82	Swindon & Cricklade Railway
36	Great Central Railway	83	Talyllyn Railway
37	Groudle Glen Railway	84	Tanfield Railway
38	Gwili Railway	85	Teifi Valley Railway
39	Heatherslaw Light Railway	86	Telford Steam Railway
40	Isle of Man Steam Railway	87	Vale of Rheidol Railway
41	Isle of Wight Steam Railway	88	Wells Harbour Railway
42	Keighley & Worth Valley Railway	89	Wells & Walsingham Railway
43	Kent & East Sussex Railway	90	Welsh Highland Railway
44	Kirklees Light Railway	91	Welshpool & Llanfair Railway
45	Lakeside & Haverthwaite Railway	92	West Lancashire Railway
46	Launceston Steam Railway	93	West Somerset Railway
47	Lavender Line		Paddlesteamer Waverley

FROM THE EDITOR

Welcome to *The Great British Steam Railway Timetable 1995*.

Firstly may I thank the many of you who took the trouble to write with your words of encouragement on the 1994 edition, and to those who also gave some suggestions for this issue – most of which have been taken on board.

These additions include railways who issue lineside photographic passes and nearby B&B establishments that are actually recommended by the railways themselves.

In these times of uncertainty on the future of our privatised national rail network, it is heartening to see many 'already private' steam lines doing so well – line extensions continue unabated such as Dean Forest's extension to Lydney Jct, and Swanage Railway's long awaited return to Corfe Castle.

At the time of writing, the Chancellor of the Exchequer is ready to impose VAT on 'fun rides'. This would naturally increase fares/admissions on steam sites who do not actually provide an A–B passenger service (try proving that!) – just one of the many issues of outside influence that affect all that we strive to do in the name of preservation. Remember that most of the railways listed in this book are wholly or largely 'volunteer run' – people preserving steam for the benefit of this generation and making sure it is there for the next.

It is a sad fact that in several cases, public transport to certain preserved lines is an impossibility – going by car seems to grate a little on the sub-conscious. However, once you have settled down into your horsehair-stuffed seat and caught that whiff of steam – you will indeed be transported back to the 'sensible age'.

Happy Travels!

ACKNOWLEDGEMENTS
Thanks to the Commercial Managers of all the entries for supplying details, to Sonia Desmond for typesetting, Eric Sawford, David Wilson, and the countless men and women of our railways, without whom we wouldn't have preserved steam at all!

COLIN TYSON

DISCLAIMER
Information correct at time of going to press. The Publishers cannot be held responsible for any inaccuracy. Visitors wishing to see particular locomotives working are advised to ring the site before travelling to check on availability.

Alderney Railway   Channel Isles

STANDARD GAUGE

HEADQUARTERS
>Alderney Railway Society, PO Box 75, Alderney, Channel Islands

PRINCIPAL STATIONS
>Braye Road, Mannez

HOW TO GET THERE
>Air: Aurigny Air Services from Southampton, Guernsey & Jersey
>Sea: Channel Island Ferries from Weymouth
>Rail: Southampton Parkway, for Southampton Airport

☎ Operations Manager 01481 823260

TIMES

| Braye Road | Dep | 14.00 | 15.00 | 16.00 |
| Mannez | Dep | 14.40 | 15.40 | 16.40 |

SERVICE OPERATES

Weekends, Bank Holidays, Easter Saturday to the end of September.
Note: The 16.00 / 16.40 train does not run between Easter and Whitsun.

1995 SPECIAL EVENTS

		FARES	
Easter Egg Specials	April 15th/16th	Adults	£1.80
Santa Trains	December 16th/17th	Child	£1.00

1 Steam Loco, 1 Diesel
Vulcan 0–4–0 DM D100 *Elizabeth*   Braye Road Station is situated on
Braye Harbour

The original line along the harbour was constructed to take stone from the quarry to the breakwaters at the harbour, back in 1847.
It is suggested that visitors telephone for steam operating dates in 1995, as the lines Bagnall has now departed, and most services will be diesel hauled.

FACILITIES
Souvenir Shop, Car Park, Disabled Facilities, Refreshments (Sundays only at Mannez).

Aberdeenshire

HEADQUARTERS
Alford Valley Railway, Alford, Aberdeenshire, AB33 8H11

PRINCIPAL STATIONS
Alford, Haughton Park, Murray Park

HOW TO GET THERE
Road: Alford is on the A944 from Aberdeen
Bus: Services from Aberdeen, but infrequent (25 miles)
Rail: Insch, 10 miles

☎ Information & Enquiries 01975 562326 (08.00 to 17.30)

TIMES

| Alford | Dep | 11.00 | 11.30 | 12.00 | 12.30 | 13.00 | 13.30 | 14.00 | 14.30 | 15.00 |
| Alford | Dep | 15.30 | 16.00 | 16.30 | 17.00 | | | | | |

Haughton Park to Murray Park trains connect with the service from Alford to Haughton Park.

The Alford to Haughton services are occasionally steam hauled, and the Haughton Park to Murray Park services are diesel hauled.

SERVICE OPERATES
Saturdays & Sundays in April, May & September. Daily in June, July & August.

FARES
Adults £1.70, Child 80p

1 Steam Loco, 3 Diesels
0–4–2 Fowler Tank Loco of 1914
Saccharine – ex-South African
sugar plantation.

BED & BREAKFAST
Sylvan   01975 562485
Henderson   01975 562159

FACILITIES
Souvenir Shop, Provision for Disabled, Nature Trail, Picnic Sites,
Transport & Heritage Centre (admission separate) at Alford, Car Park, Caravan Site.

This 2'0" gauge line at the heart of the Grampian region makes an ideal base for touring North East Scotland. The ex-Great North of Scotland Railway building at Alford is next to the heritage centre, displaying GNSR items.

NARROW GAUGE

HEADQUARTERS

Amberley (Chalk Pits) Museum, Houghton Bridge, Amberley,
Arundel, West Sussex, BN18 9LT

HOW TO GET THERE

Road: On B2139, midway between Arundel & Storrington
Rail: Amberley (adjacent). Admission discount with rail ticket
River: Regular launch service from Arundel & Littlehampton
Tel 01243 265792

☎ Information / Enquiries 01798 831370   Fax 01798 831831

TIMES

10.00 to 18.00. Last admission 17.00. Trains operate to demand.

Open from March 22nd to October 29th,
Wednesdays to Sundays & Bank Holiday Mondays.
Open daily during local school holidays.

SPECIAL EVENT   July 1st/2nd Railway Gala Weekend

No fares are charged. The Railway is one part of a 36 acre open-air Industrial
History Museum.
Admission: Adults £4.50, Child £2.10, Family £11.50
The Railway incorporates the ex-Brockham collection of Industrial Narrow gauge locos and
rolling stock incl. Decauville 0–4–0 *Barbouillier*, Bagnall 2–4–0T *Polar Bear*, Bagnall
0–4–0ST *Peter*, Baldwin 4–6–0T *Lion*, Fletcher Jennings 0–4–0T *Townsend Hook*,
Pecket 0–6–0T *Scaldwell*.

Museum recommends allowing a minimum of three hours to get the most out of any visit.

FACILITIES

Souvenir Shop, Light Refreshments, Disabled access, Picnic Site, Car Park.
Site Includes: blacksmith shop, potters workshop, print works, boatbuilders, engineers and
wheelwright workshop, Southdown bus garage, steam road vehicles, stationary engines,
village garage, vintage wireless exhibition, amateur radio station, telephone exchange,
domestic bygones, timberyard etc.
Winner of 'Best Museum in the South of England' from the AA.

Avon

STANDARD GAUGE

HEADQUARTERS
      Bitton Station, Willsbridge, Bristol BS15 6ED, Avon

PRINCIPAL STATION
      Bitton

HOW TO GET THERE
      Road: On A431, halfway between Bristol and Bath
      Bus: Badgerline Service 332 (Bristol–Bath)
      Rail: Keynsham, 2 miles

☎ Information 0117 932 7296   Weekends 0117 932 5538

TIMES

Bitton	Dep	11.00	12.00	13.00	14.00	15.00	16.00	17.00
Oldland	Dep	11.20	12.20	13.20	14.20	15.20	16.20	17.20
Bitton	Arr	11.26	12.26	13.26	14.26	15.26	16.26	17.26
Bitton	Dep	11.35	12.35	13.35	14.35	15.35	16.35	17.35
Fieldgrove	Dep	11.43	12.43	13.43	14.43	15.43	16.43	- - - -
Bitton	Arr	11.47	12.47	13.47	14.47	15.47	16.47	- - - -

No alighting at Oldland and Field Grove.
Bitton–Oldland section, trains alternate between steam/diesel.
Bitton–Field Grove section, steam and diesel 'top and tail'.

Station open every weekend 11.00–17.00 for static viewing.

SERVICE OPERATES
April 14th–17th. May 7th/8th, 28th/29th. June 4th, 11th, 18th, 25th.
July 2nd, 9th, 16th, 23rd, 30th. August Sundays & 28th. September Sundays.
October 1st. Santa Trains. December weekends.

1995 SPECIAL EVENT
Railway Art Exhibition   August 27th/28th.

FARES
Adults   £3.00, OAP   £2.00
Child   £1.00, Family   £7.50
Unlimited travel on day of issue.

Length of operating line 1½ miles

1995 LOCOS
Hunslet 0–6–0 ST *Darfield No 1*
BR 07 0–6–0 D2994

9 Steam Locos, 3 Diesels.

· 1995 will see the first full year of operation on the newly-opened
Southern extension towards Bath.

FACILITIES
Souvenir Shop, Light Refreshments, Car Park, Picnic Site, Disabled access on train.

Ayrshire Railway Ayrshire

SCOTTISH INDUSTRIAL RAILWAY CENTRE   STANDARD GAUGE

HEADQUARTERS
Minnivey Colliery, Burnton, Dalmellington, Ayrshire

HOW TO GET THERE

Raod:	On A173 Ayr–Castle Douglas road, signposted
Bus:	Western Scottish Services, Ayr– Castle Douglas
Rail:	Ayr, 16 miles

☎ 01292 313579   evenings
01292 531144   daytime for steam dates and special event information

TIMES

11.00 to 16.00

Saturdays June–September (static)
Please telephone for steam operating days. (Brake van rides available.)

The preservation group acquired a greenfield site at the disused Minnivey Colliery in 1980, and based on a colliery line operation, now provide steam services on open days in conjunction with a museum of mining, also based in the former colliery.

The standard gauge locos are mainly ex-National Coal Board and go a long way in explaining the Scottish Industrial railway scene. (9 Steam Locos.)

Steam crane and various items of rolling stock on display.

2'6" gauge line.

FACILITIES

Souvenir Shop, Light Refreshments, some provision for Disabled, Car Park, Museum.

Gwynedd

NARROW GAUGE

HEADQUARTERS
The Station, Llanuwchllyn, Bala, Gwynedd, LL23 7DD

PRINCIPAL STATIONS
Llanuwchllyn, Llangower, Bala

HOW TO GET THERE
Road: A494 (from M56 or M54 then A5 to A494)
Rail: Wrexham, 38 miles, Barmouth, 25 miles

☎ Information 01678 540666

TIMES

		A	B	A	B	A	B	A	B	A
Llanuwchllyn	Dep	11.00	11.15	12.30	12.50	14.00	14.25	15.30	16.00	17.00
Bala	Arr	11.25	11.40	12.55	13.15	14.25	14.50	15.55	16.25	17.25
Bala	Dep	11.35	11.50	13.05	13.25	14.35	15.00	16.05	16.35	17.35
Llanuwchllyn	Arr	12.00	12.15	13.30	13.50	15.00	15.25	16.30	17.00	17.55

SERVICE OPERATES

TABLE A.   May 28th and 29th and August 27th and 28th.

TABLE B.   Daily April 14th–30th except April 24th and 28th.
May 2nd–31st except Fridays and 15th, 22nd, 28th and 29th.
Daily June except Mondays, and Fridays 9th, 16th, 23rd and 30th.
Daily July and August except August 27th and 28th.
Daily September except Mondays, and Fridays 8th, 15th, 22nd, 29th.
October 1st.
Last train departures from Bala are for SINGLE journey only.
Extra trains may run on Bank Holidays and during peak periods.

1995 SPECIAL EVENTS

Teddy Bears' Weekend   July 22nd/23rd
Fireworks Extravaganza   November 4th
Santa Trains   December 9th/10th

Running through the Snowdonia National Park and along the shores of Wales' largest natural lake, the line is ideal for views not normally seen from the roadside.

FARES
Adults £5.00 return
Children £3.00
Family Savers
1 Adult + 1 Child £6.00
2 Adults + 1 Child £11.00
Each additional child £1.00

Length of operating line 4½ miles

3 Steam Locos, *Holy War,*
Maid Marian, Triassic

FACILITIE5
Souvenir Shop, Picnic Site, Disabled Carriage access, Loco Shed, Light Refreshments.

THE BATTLEFIELD LINE   STANDARD GAUGE

HEADQUARTERS
     Shackerstone Station, Shackerstone, Nr. Nuneaton, Warks, CV13 6NW

PRINCIPAL STATIONS
     Shackerstone, Market Bosworth, Shenton

HOW TO GET THERE
     Road: On B585 off A444 Nuneaton–Burton-on-Trent road
     Rail: Nuneaton, 9 miles

 Information 01827 880754

TIMES – Sundays

		A			B	B	C
Shackerstone	Dep	11.00	12.30	14.00	15.25	16.50	16.00
Mkt Bosworth	Dep	11.15	12.45	14.15	15.40	17.05	16.15
Shenton	Arr	11.25	12.55	14.25	15.50	17.15	16.25
Shenton	Dep	11.35	13.05	14.35	16.00	17.25	16.35
Mkt Bosworth	Dep	11.45	13.15	14.45	16.10	17.35	16.45
Shackerstone	Arr	12.00	13.30	15.00	16.25	17.50	17.00

NOTES: A. This train runs on Bank Holiday weekends only.
               B. These trains do not run on Sundays in October.
               C. This train only runs on Sundays in October.

SERVICE OPERATES

     Sundays and Bank Holidays from Easter until end of October.

TIMES – Saturdays

		D	D	D
Shackerstone	Dep	13.00	14.45	16.15
Shenton	Arr	13.18	15.03	16.33
Shenton	Dep	13.30	15.15	16.45
Shackerstone	Arr	13.48	15.33	17.03

All trains call at Market Bosworth

NOTE: D
The Saturday Diesel service may be replaced by Steam on Bank Holidays/Special Events.

SERVICE OPERATES
     Saturdays May 6th to end of September and are Diesel hauled.
     Wednesdays in June, July and August.

1995 SPECIAL EVENTS

Easter Eggstras	April 16th/17th
Teddy Bears' Picnic	May 7th/8th
Thomas Weekend	May 27th–29th
Steam Fair (prop)	August 5th/6th
Postman Pat	October 29th
Santa Trains	Weekends in December until Sunday 24th.

FARES

Adult	£4.50 return
Child/OAP	£2.25
Family	£12.00

9 Steam Locos, 6 Diesels

1995 LOCOS
Mainly ex-industrial tanks with visiting BR loco to be confirmed.

WINE & DINE
The *Tudor Rose* Dining service operates April 23rd, May 21st, June 11th, July 16th, August 20th & September 17th.

Length of operating line
4¾ miles

The operating society celebrated their 25th year in 1994, and are now reaping the benefits of the longer ride to Shenton.

FACILITIES
Souvenir Shop, Light Refreshments, Full Meals, Buffet / Bar on train, Museum, Picnic Site, Car Park, Lineside Passes – apply Operations Manager.

The Severn Valley Railway's Ivatt looks perfectly at home with a 'Cardigan Bay Express' tour through Barmouth, North Wales

Paul Appleton

Sussex

35th ANNIVERSARY YEAR – 1995   STANDARD GAUGE

HEADQUARTERS
Sheffield Park Station, Nr Uckfield, East Sussex, TN22 3QL

PRINCIPAL STATIONS
Sheffield Park, Horsted Keynes, Kingscote

HOW TO GET THERE
Road: A275 midway between Lewes and East Grinstead
Bus: All trains have bus connection to East Grinstead BR
to/from Kingscote
Rail: East Grinstead, 2 miles

☎ Information 01825 722370 Enquiries 01825 723777
Catering/ Hotel Train 01825 722008   Fax 01825 724139

TIMES

TABLE A

Sheffield Park	Dep	11.00	12.30	14.00	15.30
Horsted Keynes	Arr	11.15	12.45	14.15	15.45
Horsted Keynes	Dep	11.17	12.47	14.17	15.47
Kingscote	Arr	11.32	13.02	14.32	16.02
Kingscote	Dep	11.47	13.17	14.47	16.17
Horsted Keynes	Arr	12.00	13.30	15.00	16.30
Horsted Keynes	Dep	12.02	13.32	15.02	16.32
Sheffield Park	Arr	12.15	13.45	15.15	16.45

TABLE A OPERATES
March 4th/5th, 11th/12th, 18th, 25th/26th. April 1st, 8th, 18th–21st, 24th–29th.
May 1st–5th, 9th–12th, 15th–19th, 22nd–26th, 30th/31st. June daily except weekends.
July 3rd–7th, 10th–14th, 17th–21st. September 4th–8th, 11th–15th, 18th–22nd, 25th–29th.
October 7th, 14th, 21st, 23rd–28th. November weekends except 11th. December 26th–31st.

TABLE B

Sheffield Park	Dep	11.00	12.00	13.00	14.00	15.00	16.00	17.00
Horsted Keynes	Arr	11.15	12.15	13.15	14.15	15.15	16.15	17.15
Horsted Keynes	Dep	11.20	12.20	13.20	14.20	15.20	16.20	-- --
Kingscote	Arr	11.35	12.35	13.35	14.25	15.35	16.35	-- --
Kingscote	Dep	-- --	11.50	12.50	13.50	14.50	15.50	16.50
Horsted Keynes	Arr	-- --	12.05	13.05	14.05	15.05	16.05	17.05
Horsted Keynes	Dep	11.17	12.17	13.17	14.17	15.17	16.17	17.17
Sheffield Park	Arr	11.30	12.30	13.30	14.30	15.30	16.30	17.30

TABLE B OPERATES
April 2nd, 9th, 22nd/23rd, 30th. May 6th, 13th, 20th. June weekends except 24th/25th.
July weekends and 22nd–28th and 31st. August daily except Sundays and Bank Holidays.
September 1st and weekends. October Sundays except 22nd.

TABLE C

```
Sheffield Park  Dep  -- --  10.40 11.30 12.20 13.10 14.00 14.50 15.40 16.30 17.20
Horsted Keynes Arr  -- --  10.55 11.45 12.35 13.25 14.15 15.05 15.55 16.45 17.35
Horsted Keynes Dep  10.07 10.57 11.47 12.37 13.27 14.17 15.07 15.57 16.47 -- --
Kingscote      Arr  10.20 11.10 12.00 12.50 13.40 14.30 15.20 16.10 17.00 -- --

Kingscote      Dep  10.35 11.25 12.15 13.05 13.55 14.45 15.35 16.25 17.15 -- --
Horsted Keynes Arr  10.48 11.38 12.28 13.18 14.08 14.58 15.48 16.38 17.28 -- --
Horsted Keynes Dep  11.00 11.50 12.40 13.30 14.20 15.10 16.00 16.50 17.40 -- --
Sheffield Park  Arr  11.13 12.03 12.53 13.43 14.33 15.23 16.13 17.03 17.53 -- --
```

TABLE C OPERATES
April 14th–17th. May 7th/8th, 14th, 21st, 27th–29th. August 6th, 13th, 20th, 27th/28th.

A Special Timetable operates on Special Event days shown below.

1995 SPECIAL EVENTS

Enthusiasts Weekend	March 19th
Childrens Fun Weekend	May 27th-29th
Steam Gala	June 24th/25th
Swapmeet	July 22nd/23rd
Steam Fair & Vintage Weekend	July 29th/30th
35th Anniversary	August 5th
Giants of Steam	October 22nd
Starlight Special Day	November 11th
Santa Trains	December Weekends

BUS CONNECTION
*Special bus to Kingscote from East Grinstead
BR leaves:
Table A 11.25 12.55 14.25 15.55
Table B 11.20 12.20 13.20 14.20 15.20 16.20
Table C 09.55 10.45 11.35 12.25 13.15 14.05
14.55

NB – There is NO Public Car Parking at Kingscote Station. Park & Ride from East Grinstead, then by special bus.
*Through fares from any BR station.

FARES

Adults £7.00, Children (3 – 15) £3.50
Family (2 Adults and up to 3 Children) £19.00.
All tickets valid for unlimited travel.

WINE & DINE
Golden Arrow Pullman
Saturday Evenings/Sunday Lunch

BED & BREAKFAST
'The Queen of Scots' Hotel Train
Sheffield Park Station 01825 722008

30 Steam Locos NO DIESELS. **LINESIDE PHOTO PASSES:** £5 Members, £15 Non Members

1995 LOCOS – 96, 323, 263, 592, 847, C1, 35027, 73082, 92240.

A Grandfather of preservation, the Bluebell is almost a household name and will be celebrating its 35th year in style. With the extension to Kingscote now complete, Horsted Keynes has returned to a 'through station', adding even more atmosphere to its Southern elegance. A favourite with the filming industry, Bluebell is just two miles short of its ultimate aim of connecting with the main rail network at East Grinstead. Until then, take the preserved bus link and enjoy!

FACILITIES
Souvenir Shop, Light Refreshments, Full Meals, Licensed Bar, On-Train Buffet, Museum, Hotel Train, Disabled Toilet, Picnic Site, Car Park, Footplate Courses.

Bodmin & Wenford Railway   Cornwall

HEADQUARTERS
Bodmin General Station, Bodmin, Cornwall, PL31 1AQ

PRINCIPAL STATIONS
Bodmin General, Bodmin Parkway

HOW TO GET THERE

Road: South of Bodmin town centre on B3268 Lostwithiel Road
Bus: Western National Services
Rail: Bodmin Parkway (adjacent)

☎ Information 01208 73666 / 74878

TIMES

TABLE A – OFF PEAK

Bodmin General	Dep	11.30	13.45	15.20
Colesloggett Halt	Dep	11.43	13.58	15.33
Bodmin Parkway	Arr	11.50	14.05	15.40

Bodmin Parkway	Dep	12.05	14.20	16.00
Colesloggett Halt	Dep	12.15	14.30	16.10
Bodmin General	Arr	12.30	14.45	16.25

This service is diesel hauled on June 3rd, 10th, 24th. September 16th, 30th.

TABLE A OPERATES
April 12th–15th, 18th–21st, 26th. May 3rd, 9th–12th, 17th, 24th, 30th/31st.
June 1st–3rd, 5th–10th, 12th–16th, 19th–24th, 26th–30th. July 1st
September 11th–16th, 18th–22nd, 25th–30th. October 4th, 11th, 18th, 25th.

TABLE B – PEAK (Mondays to Saturdays)

						PS
Bodmin General	Dep	11.10	12.35	14.25	16.10	19.00
Colesloggett Halt	Dep	11.23	12.48	14.38	16.23	19.13
Bodmin Parkway	Arr	11.30	12.55	14.45	16.30	19.20

Bodmin Parkway	Dep	11.45	13.10	15.05	16.45	19.45
Colesloggett Halt	Dep	11.55	13.20	15.15	16.55	19.55
Bodmin General	Arr	12.10	13.35	15.30	17.10	20.10

TABLE B OPERATES
April 17th. May 8th, 29th. July 3rd–8th, 10th–14th, 17th–22nd, 24th–29th, 31st.
August 1st–5th, 7th–12th, 14th–19th, 21st–26th, 28th–31st. September 1st, 4th–8th.

PS: Pasty Special Tuesdays and Thursdays only July 18th–August 31st.
This service is diesel hauled on July 8th, 22nd, 29th and all Saturdays in August.

TABLE C – PEAK (Sundays Only)

Bodmin General	Dep	11.15	12.40	14.25	16.10
Colesloggett Halt	Dep	11.28	12.53	14.38	16.23
Bodmin Parkway	Arr	11.35	13.00	14.45	16.30
Bodmin Parkway	Dep	11.50	13.15	15.00	16.45
Colesloggett Halt	Dep	12.00	13.25	15.10	16.55
Bodmin General	Arr	12.15	13.40	15.25	17.10

TABLE C OPERATES
April 9th, 16th, 23rd, 30th. May 7th, 14th, 21st, 28th. June 4th, 11th, 25th.
August 6th, 13th, 20th, 27th. September 17th. October 1st, 8th, 15th, 22nd, 29th.

TABLE D – 1995 SPECIAL EVENTS
A Special Service will operate on the following dates.

Steam & Diesel Gala	June 17th/18th	**OTHER SPECIAL EVENTS**
Thomas Weekends	July 15th/16th	VE-Day 50th Anniv — May 8th
	September 2nd/3rd	Teddy Bear Specials — Aug 16th
	November 4th/5th	Santa Specials — Dec 9th/10th
Steam Gala	September 9th/10th	16th/17th,
Diesel Gala	September 23rd/24th	22nd, 24th

Mince Pie
Rambler Trains from December 26th.

FARES
Adults £4.90, OAP £4.50
Child £2.80, Family £13.50

The Bodmin & Wenford Railway has slowly extended itself from its Bodmin General base, and now connects with the mainline at Bodmin Parkway. A lovely line with stone bridges and stations and superb scenery.

FACILITIES
Souvenir Shop, Buffet, Car Park, Heritage Centre.

Bicycles can be hired in Wadebridge and railway reached via 'Camel trail'.
Length of operating line 3½ miles

PURE NOSTALGIA!

Cornwall's only
preserved
branchline

Bodmin & Wenford

General Station, Bodmin (0208) 73666

Bo'ness and Kinneil Railway

W.Lothian

'The Forth Valley Line'   STANDARD GAUGE

HEADQUARTERS
Bo'ness Station, Union Street, Bo'ness, West Lothian, EH51 9AQ
PRINCIPAL STATIONS
Bo'ness, Birkhill
HOW TO GET THERE
Road: M9 then A904
Rail: Linlithgow, then 3 miles by bus
Bus: Tel 01506 842167, routes 35, 50, 204, 234/5/6

☎   Information 01506 822298

TIMES

Bo'ness	Dep	11.30	13.00	14.15	15.30	16.30
Birkhill	Arr	11.47	13.17	14.32	15.47	16.47
Birkhill	Dep	12.05	13.35	14.50	16.05	- - - -
Bo'ness	Arr	12.22	13.52	15.07	16.22	- - - -

Table runs all operating dates except Special Events.

SERVICE OPERATES:
Every weekend April 1st – October 15th.
Daily July 8th – August 20th. Mondays April 17th, May 1st, 29th.

1995 SPECIAL EVENTS

Easter Egg Specials	April 15th–17th
Friends of *Thomas*	May 13th/14th
Teddy Bears' Day	June 11th
Vintage Vehicle Rally	June 18th
Friends of *Thomas*	August 13th/14th
Commercial Vehicle Rally	Sept 17th
Diesel Weekend	Sept 23rd/24th

BED & BREAKFAST

Chestnut Lodge	01506 826420
Hollywood House	01506 823260

FARES
Adults £3.60, Child £1.80,
Family £9.00

4 Steam Locos, 6 Diesels

1995 LOCOS
No. 673 *Maude* NCB No. 19

Length of operating line 3½ miles

Scottish Railway Exhibition
Opening in 1995

Just out of sight of the Forth Bridge, the Forth Valley Line gives a uniquely Scottish flavour, both locos and stations. At Birkhill you can visit an underground clay mine.

FACILITIES
Souvenir Shop, Light Refreshments, Museum, Picnic Site, Car Park, Photographic Passes.

Tyne & Wear

STANDARD GAUGE

HEADQUARTERS
Springwell Village, Gateshead, Tyne & Wear, NE9 7QJ
PRINCIPAL STATIONS
Springwell, Blackham's Hill
HOW TO GET THERE
Road: On B1288 off A1 (M)
Bus: Go-Ahead Northern, 187–189, x4, x5
Rail: Newcastle, 4 miles, Gateshead (Metro), 2 miles

☎ Enquiries 0191 416 1847

TIMES

Trains operate from 11.00 to 17.00 at approx. 30 minute intervals, on the dates below.
Open for static display Saturdays 10.00 to 16.00.

SERVICE OPERATES

First Sunday of each month from Easter til end of September.
Also Bank Holiday Mondays and other 'Special Events'.
Please confirm details by phoning.

1995 SPECIAL EVENTS (provisional)
Easter Bunny Weekend April 16th/17th
VE-Day Event   May 7th
Friends of *Thomas*
the Tank Engine   May 17th/18th
Vintage Vehicle Weekend July 2nd
Family Fun Day   August 6th
Santa Specials   Dec 9th/10th
                    16th/17th

FARES

Adult	£2.50
Child/OAP	£1.50
Family	£7.00

Includes train ride and admission to
Site / Museum. Subject to revision.
Prices may alter on Special Event Days.

The world's only preserved Standard gauge rope-hauled railway, giving unique rope haulage demonstrations, steam rides and unique, historic workshops complex.

1995 LOCOS
Andrew Barclay 0–4–0 ST 2274/1949
Andrew Barclay 0–4–0 ST 2361/1954

3 Steam Locos, 4 Diesels

Length of operating line 1¼ miles

FACILITIES
Souvenir Shop, Museum, Light Refreshments, Car Park, Picnic Site, Disabled Toilet.

Mid-Glamorgan

BRECON MOUNTAIN RAILWAY

NARROW GAUGE

HEADQUARTERS
> Pant Station, Dowlais, Merthyr Tydfil, Mid-Glamorgan, CF48 2UP

PRINCIPAL STATION
> Pant

HOW TO GET THERE
> Road: Off the A465, 3 miles north of Merthyr Tydfil signposted
> 'Mountain Railway'
> Bus: Service from Merthyr Tydfil Bus station to Pant Cemetery (not Suns)
> Rail: Merthyr Tydfil, 3 miles

☎ Information 01685 722988. Fax 01685 384854

TIMES

A	Pant	Dep	-- --	12.00	13.00	14.00	15.00	16.00	-- --	
B	Pant	Dep	11.00	12.00	13.00	14.00	15.00	16.00	17.00	
C	Pant	Dep	11.00	12.00	13.00	14.00	15.00	16.00	-- --	

Round trip time 50 minutes, unless you break journey at Pontsticill and return by later train.

SERVICE OPERATES

Table A – April 2nd, 9th, 23rd, 30th. May 14th, 21st.
> September 10th, 17th, 24th. October 1st, 8th, 15th, 22nd, 29th.

Table B – April 16th/17th. May 7th/8th, 28th/29th.
> June 4th, 11th, 18th, 25th. July 2nd, 9th, 16th, 23rd, 30th.
> August 6th, 13th, 20th, 27th/28th. September 3rd.

Table C – April 14th/15th, 18th–22nd, 25th–27th and 29th.
> May 2nd–4th, 6th, 9th–11th, 13th, 16th–18th, 20th, 23rd–25th, 27th, 30th/31st.
> June – daily except Sundays. July – daily except Sundays.
> August – daily except Sundays and August 28th.
> September 1st/2nd, 4th–7th, 9th, 12th–14th, 16th, 19th–21st, 23rd, 26th–28th, 30th.
> October 3rd–5th, 10th–12th, 17th–19th, 24th–26th.

SANTA SPECIALS
December weekends preceeding Christmas.

Steam into the Brecon Beacons National Park. This year sees an extension of a further 3½ miles from Pontsticill to Dolygaer, by the side of Taf Fechan Reservoir.

FARES

Adult	£5.00
First Child	£1.00
Extra Children	£2.50

includes admission to loco workshop

9 Steam Locos, 2 Diesels **1995 LOCO**
0–6–2 WTT *Graf Schwerin Lowitz*

BED & BREAKFAST
The Signal Box c/o BMR

FACILITIES
Souvenir Shop, Light Refreshments, Disabled Toilet & train access, Picnic Site, Car Park, Full Meals.

Bristol Harbour Railway Avon

HEADQUARTERS

Bristol Industrial Museum, Princes Wharf, City Docks, Bristol, Avon, BS9 4RN

PRINCIPAL STATIONS

Industrial Museum, Wapping Wharf (for SS *Great Britain*)

HOW TO GET THERE

Road: off M5, docks are in the city centre

Bus: via City centre. City Line / Badger Line

Rail: Temple Meads, ¾ mile

☎ Enquiries 0117 925 1470 Fax 0117 929 7318

TIMES

12.00 to 18.00 at 15 minute intervals between Industrial Museum and Maritime Heritage Centre (within SS *Great Britain*).

SERVICE OPERATES (Railway Steaming dates)

March 18th/19th. April 1st/2nd, 15th–17th.
May 6th–8th, 27th–29th.
June 17th/18th. July 8th/9th, 29th/30th.
August 12th/13th, 26th–28th.
September 9th/10th, 23rd/24th.
October 7th/8th, 21st/22nd, 28th/29th.

Access is not available to Locos on non Steam dates.

1995 SPECIAL EVENTS
Steam Festival July 8th/9th

Steam Tug *Mayflower* operates from the docks on various weekends between March and October.

Length of operating line ½ mile

Built to link the docks with the mainline railways.
Several of the former Harbour Co's wagons are on display.
Combine with trip to the Maritime Centre within the giant SS *Great Britain*.

FARES

Return 80p
Single 50p
Under 6 Free

3 Steam Locos
Bristol-built 0–6–0 ST
Avonside *Portbury*
Peckett *Henbury*
1 Diesel Loco

FACILITIES
Souvenir Shop, Industrial Museum, Heritage Centre at SS *Great Britain*,
Disabled Toilet, Car Park.

Bucks

STANDARD GAUGE

HEADQUARTERS
Quainton Road Station, Quainton, Nr Aylesbury, Bucks, HP22 4BY

PRINCIPAL STATION
Quainton Road

HOW TO GET THERE
Road: Signposted from A41 at Waddesdon, 5 miles north of Aylesbury
Bus: Aylesbury Bus Ltd, from Aylesbury. Tel 01296 23445
Rail: Aylesbury, 7 miles

☎ Talking Timetable 01296 655450   Enquiries/Fax 01296 655720

TIMES
Steam Days 11.00 to 17.00
Non Steam Days 11.00 to 16.00

TRAINS OPERATE

Steam Days: Every Sunday and Bank Holiday Monday April to October inclusive at 20 minute intervals.

Non Steam Days for static viewing: Sundays in January, February, March and Saturdays April to October inclusive.

1995 SPECIAL EVENTS

Easter Fun Days	April 16th/17th
VE-Day Celebrations	May 7th/8th
Vintage Transport Festival	May 28th/29th
Miniature Gala	June 3rd/4th
Friends of *Thomas the Tank Engine*	July 1st/2nd
Ladies Day	July 16th
Locomotion Visit	August 27th/28th
Firefighting Day	September 17th
Friends of *Thomas the Tank Engine*	September 23rd
Santa Specials	December T.B.A.

FARES
Adults   £4.00   Child/OAP   £3.00
Family   £14.00 2 Adults, up to 4 Children
Special prices for *Thomas* Events,
Santas and planned Aylesbury shuttles.
Prices include unlimited rides.

2 x ½ mile demonstration lines, at the heart of John Betjemen's 'Metroland' – Steam on the 'Met' is alive and well.

30 Steam Locos, 6 Diesels

1995 LOCOS
L99 Pannier Tank ex GWR,LT
Coventry No. 1 North British Tank Loco
Peckett Tank 2087

BED & BREAKFAST
The White Hart   01296 655234

FACILITIES
Souvenir Shop, Light Refreshments, Car Park, Disabled Facilities, Museum, Picnic Site, Footplate Courses, Full Meals.

10th

Season

RAILWAY HOLIDAYS

Setting the pace -

Unique railway touring holidays, with the emphasis on preserved railways - full of fun and good company.

Holiday areas for 1995 focus on:

- THE LAKE DISTRICT
- ISLE OF MAN
- DERBYSHIRE
- HOLLAND
- THE NORTH EAST
- HANTS & ALDERNEY
- SNOWDONIA
- DEVON & CORNWALL
- HARZ MOUNTAINS

- SOMERSET
- SUSSEX
- METROLAND
- BELGIUM
- SCOTLAND
- YORKSHIRE
- NORFOLK
- FRANCE
- COTSWOLDS

See and ride all the major attractions in each of the above areas.
Inside Track is the only holiday company providing a comprehensive programme of railway holidays for you, your friends and family in Britain, France, Belgium and Holland.
Please call us or write for our brochure because you are missing out on a good free read and then the opportunity to experience for yourself why we are setting the pace.
So, to steam up and away with Inside Track, send for your full colour brochure now:

**Inside Track, Dept TT,
1 Castle Street, Berkhamsted, Hertfordshire HP4 2BQ.
Or call (01442) 872995 (24 hours). Fax (01442) 877217.**

Norfolk

HEADQUARTERS
Aylsham Station, Norwich Road, Aylsham, Norfolk, NR11 6BW

PRINCIPAL STATIONS
Aylsham, Wroxham

HOW TO GET THERE
Road: On A140 Norwich / Cromer Road
Bus: Information 01603 613613
Rail: Hoveton & Wroxham, 200 yds

☎ Information 01263 733858   Fax 01263 733814

TIMES

Aylsham   Departures from 10.15–15.15 (until 16.30 High Season)
Wroxham   Departures from 11.30–16.30 (until 17.35 High Season)

Easter until October 29th
Full timetable not available at present. Advisable to telephone before travelling.

FARES
Adults   £6.50, Child £4.00
Family   £17.50
(2 Adults and up to 3 Children)
Off-Peak fares cheaper.

Boat Train inclusive tickets
Adult £9, Child £5.50
Off-Peak fares cheaper.

4 Steam Locos, 2 Diesel
Length of operating line 9 miles

BOAT TRAINS
Trains departing Aylsham at 10.15 and 12.45 are timed to connect with boat trips
(duration 1½ hours) from Wroxham Bridge. Sundays to Thursdays only between
May and September.

Now in its third management, the Bure Valley Railway has had a bumpy start to its short life.
Built on the track bed of the former Great Eastern Railway Wroxham – County School route
(County School is another preservation location – see Mid-Norfolk Railway entry at rear of
book), the 15" gauge line regularly hires Romney, Hythe & Dymchurch locos.

FACILITIES

Souvenir Shop, Light Refreshments, Full Meals, Museum, Disabled Toilet, Picnic Site,
Car Park, Footplate Course.

Cadeby Light Railway   Leics

NARROW GAUGE

HEADQUARTERS
> The Old Rectory, Cadeby, Nuneaton, CV13 0AS

HOW TO GET THERE
> Road: On A447, 6 miles north of Hinckley
> Bus: Midland Fox 01162 511411
> Rail: Hinckley, 6 miles

☎   01455 290462

TIMES
> 13.00–17.00.

> Public open days on the second Saturday of every month, plus August 13th, November 4th, December 9th, 16th & 26th. January 13th 1996.

> Private parties at other times by arrangement.

> Narrow Gauge railway and 5" gauge railway are part of The Cadeby Experience. Includes agricultural road vehicles, model railway, The Boston Museum & Brass Rubbing Centre.

> No admission fee – donations to upkeep of railway.

> Loco: Bagnall 0–4–0 ST *Pixie* of 1919   75 yard operating line

FACILITIES

Light Refreshments and full meals for parties by arrangement.

Museum, Souvenir Shop, Car Park.

BED & BREAKFAST
Red Lion Inn   01455 291713
Bosworth Firs   01455 290727

The Late Revd Teddy Boston's collection is maintained by his wife and volunteers within the rectory grounds.

1995 SPECIAL EVENTS

32nd Anniversary	April 8th
Vintage Day	July 8th
Steam & Country Fayre	August 12/13th
Mini Traction Engines	September 9th
Bonfire Special	November 4th
Santa Specials	December 9th/16th

Caledonian Railway (Brechin) Tayside

STANDARD GAUGE

HEADQUARTERS
> The Station, 2 Park Road, Brechin, DD9 7AF

PRINCIPAL STATIONS
> Brechin, Bridge of Dun

HOW TO GET THERE

Road:	Off A94 – follow Montrose signs through town centre to Southesk Street, or via A935 from Montrose, second left in Southesk Street signed Tourist Information and station is directly ahead. (A90 from Dundee–Aberdeen)
Rail:	Montrose, 9 miles from Brechin, 4 miles from Bridge of Dun
Bus:	Strathtay Scottish 01382 228054/227201

☎ Information 01356 622992 Enquiries 01674 81318 or 01334 55965

TIMES – Summer Sundays

Brechin	Dep	11.25	12.25	13.40	14.40	15.55	17.25
Bridge of Dun	Dep	10.25	11.55	13.10	14.10	15.25	16.45

SERVICE OPERATES

> Steam Days: Sundays only May 28th–September 10th (incl. Special Events)
> Diesel Days: Wednesdays July 5th–August 23rd

1995 SPECIAL EVENTS

Easter Egg Specials	April 16th
Teddy Bears Picnic	May 28th/Jul 30th
Victorian Weekend	June 10th/11th
Fathers Day	June 18th
Gala Day	July 9th
Real Ale Festival	August 12th/13th
Nursery Rhyme Day	August 27th
Halloween	October 29th
Santa Specials	December 10th,17th, 24th.

FARES

Adult   £4.00, Child   £2.00
Family   £12.00

7 Steam Locos, 10 Diesels

Length of operating line 4 miles

1995 LOCO
1944 Bagnall *Austerity*
0–6–0 ST

The sites at Brechin and at Bridge of Dun are open for viewing most weekends. Worth including on your next Scottish tour – this once part of the mighty Caledonian Railway System.

FACILITIES
Souvenir Shop, Light Refreshments, Disabled Toilet, Picnic Site, Car Park.
Santa Trains depart Brechin only. Joint ticketing with the Historic House of Dun (National Trust for Scotland property) in summer season.

Chasewater Steam Railway

W.Midlands

The Colliery Line

STANDARD GAUGE

HEADQUARTERS
Brownhills West Station, Hednesford Road, Brownhills West, Walsall, WS8 7LT

PRINCIPAL STATIONS
Brownhills West, Norton Lakeside (1½ mile line)

HOW TO GET THERE

Road: On Pool Road off A5 southbound carriageway at Brownhills
Bus: West Midlands Travel No. 156, Sundays, hourly from Birmingham
Rail: Walsall (not Sundays) or Birmingham New Street

☎ Information 01543 452623 or 0121 384 5081

NORMAL OPERATING SEASON
Easter then Sundays & Bank Holidays April to early October.

9 Steam Locos, 5 Diesels   **FARES** Adults £1.95, Child £1.10, Family £4.95

This former Midland line runs through the Chasewater Park complex.

FACILITIES
Souvenir Shop, Light Refreshments, Buffet, Car Park, Disabled Coach.

Thundersley, built in 1909 for the LTSR, making one of its rare outside appearances at Bressingham Steam Museum, Norfolk

Eric Sawford

29

Cheddleton Railway Centre

Staffs

Churnet Valley Railway

STANDARD GAUGE

HEADQUARTERS
Cheddleton Station, Nr Leek, Staffordshire, ST13 7EE
PRINCIPAL STATION
Cheddleton
HOW TO GET THERE
Road: 3 miles from Leek on A520 Stone–Leek Road
Bus: Potteries Motor Traction. Tel 01782 747000
Rail: Stoke-on-Trent, 10 miles

☎ Information 01538 360522

TIMES
Trains run half hourly during an open day (telephone for details).
Times may alter on Special Days or due to demand.

1995 SPECIAL EVENTS

Thomas the Tank Engine	April 15th–17th
	August 26th–28th
Diesel Day	May 14th/August 6th
Model Railway Day	June 11th
Summer Fayre	July 16th
Teddy Bears Picnic	August 13th
Steam Day	August 20th
Halloween	October 29th
Santa & Steam	December 3rd, 10th, 17th

FARES
Not Yet Known

6 Steam Locos, 6 Diesels

1995 LOCOS
Kitson 0–6–0 ST *Austin 1*
Barclay 0–4–0 ST *Efficient*
Diesels, 03, 04, 08 D3420

400 yd demonstration line

BED & BREAKFAST
Prospect House   01782 550639
Railway Inn   01538 754782

Formerly known as the North Staffordshire Railway, the volunteers are hoping that if negotiations and fundraising is successful, a steam service may commence on the Churnet Valley in 1995.

The ultimate aim is to connect with BR network at Leekbrook and a new locomotive hall has been built.

The only surviving steam loco from the original North Staffordshire Railway 0–6–2 T NSR No. 2 is on display from the National Collection at York.

FACILITIES
Souvenir Shop, Light Refreshments, Museum, Car Park, Footplate Courses, Picnic Area.

STANDARD GAUGE

HEADQUARTERS
> PO Box 300, Princes Risborough, Buckinghamshire, HP27 9EL

PRINCIPAL STATION
> Chinnor Station, Station Road, Chinnor, Oxon

HOW TO GET THERE
> Road: Just off B4009, 3 miles from M40
> Rail: Princes Risborough
> Bus: Wycombe Bus Co. 232/331/332. Tel 01494 520941

☎ Timetable 01844 353535 Enquires 01296 433795

TIMES

							MS
Chinnor	Dep	11.00	12.15	13.30	14.45	16.00	17.15

SERVICE OPERATES
Every Saturday, Sunday & Bank Holiday from April to October.
MS: May to September only.

FARES
Adults £4.00   Length of operating line 3 miles
Child   £2.00
Rover   £8.00

A newcomer to a timetabled regular service, the mainstay of 1995 operations will be diesel hauled (probably Class 17), which will be supplemented by visiting steam locos.

SANTA SPECIALS
All weekends in December.

See Railway Magazines for details of other events.

LOCOS: Sentinel 4wvb 6515, Class 17 D8568, D3018 *Haversham*, Ruston Hornsby *Iris*.

FACILITIES
Souvenir Shop, Car Park, Light Refreshments, Disabled Toilet, Footplate Courses.

Cholsey & Wallingford Railway

Oxon

STANDARD GAUGE

HEADQUARTERS
>	Hithercroft Road, Wallingford, Oxfordshire, OX10 0NF

PRINCIPAL STATIONS
>	Wallingford, Cholsey *

HOW TO GET THERE
>	Road:	Wallingford Station is in St. Johns Road, off A4130 town bypass
>	Rail:	Cholsey,Thames Line trains *

☎ Enquiries 01491 835 067

TIMES

From Wallingford, from 11.00 to 17.00 at approx. 30 minute intervals.

SERVICE OPERATES
>	April 15th–17th. May 7th/8th, 28th/29th. June 18th.
>	July 23rd. August 6th, 13th, 27th/28th. September 17th, 24th.

1995 SPECIAL EVENTS

Easter Bunnies	April 16th/17th
Santa Specials	December 3rd, 10th, 16th/17th

(Santa trains only from 11.00 to 16.00)

* All services are currently based on Wallingford. A full service between Wallingford and Cholsey will be introduced during late 1995. See press for limited services from Cholsey during mid-1995, giving passengers an interchange at Cholsey with the GWR mainline.

1995 LOCOS

Length of operating line 2½ miles

Peckett 0–4–0
Austerity 0–6–0 (prov)
08 Shunter

FACILITIES – Available only on operating days

Souvenir Shop, Light Refreshments, Car Park, Museum with 'N' gauge model railway.

Cleethorpes Coast Light Railway

South Humberside

'The Lakeside Line'   MINIMUM GAUGE

HEADQUARTERS
> Kingsway Station, Kings Road, Cleethorpes, DN35 0BY

HOW TO GET THERE
> Road: King Road – main promenade access
> Bus: From Pier
> Rail: Cleethorpes, 1½ miles

☎ Information 01472 602118

TIMES From 09.00 to 20.00. Daily Easter to mid-September. Weekends until March 1996.

1995 SPECIAL EVENTS

Easter Egg Specials	April 16th/17th
Little Giants of Steam	May 13th/14th
Transport Festival	June 4th
Unusual Steam Gala	June 17th/18th
Thomas the Tank Engine	July 8th/9th
Autumn Gala	September 30th/October 1st
Spook Specials	October 29th
Sanat Trains	December 2nd/3rd, 9th/10th, 16th/17th, 23rd/24th 30th/31st

Now a 15" gauge line and one of our leading minimum gauge lines. Quite what the odd lone dog-walker along the beach makes of a passing 'Spook Special' on dark nights in October one can only hazard a guess!

FACILITIES
Souvenir Shop, Car Park, Disabled facilities (prior booking), Beach Access, Light Refreshments, Nature Walks, Santa trains December.

HEADQUARTERS
Castle Hedingham Station, Gt. Yeldham Road, Castle Hedingham, Halstead, Essex, CO9 3DZ

PRINCIPAL STATION
Castle Hedingham

HOW TO GET THERE
Road: Off A604 between Hedingham and Gt. Yeldham
Bus: Hedingham Coaches
Rail: Braintree, 7 miles

 Information & General Enquiries 01787 461174

TIMES
Trains depart at frequent intervals from 12.00 to 16.30.
11.00 to 16.30 on Bank Holidays.

SERVICE OPERATES
Sundays from March 26th until end of October.
Saturdays, Sundays & Mondays on Bank Holiday weekends.
Tuesdays, Wednesdays & Thursdays in school summer holidays.
Diesel Hauled – some Saturdays. Also Fridays in school holidays.

FARES
Adults   £4.00, Child   £2.00
OAP   £3.00, Family   £10.00

Length of operating line 1 mile

Site is open for static display from March to December

8 Steam Locos, 8 Diesels

WINE & DINE
CVR Pullman Service (pre-booked) runs Saturday evenings, Sunday luncheons & private functions.

Based on the former GER Sible & Castle Hedingham Station, the railway society have always put the accent on a quality dining service (once mentioned in Egon Ronay guide) rather than preservation in its true sense. Whilst not exactly authentic, the quality of restoration to their dining coaches is first class.

FACILITIES

Souvenir Shop, Light Refreshments, Full meals, Licensed Bar, Museum, Picnic Site, Car Park, Video Carriage, Educational Service (advanced booking only).

Dean Forest Railway

Glos.

'The Friendly Forest Line'   **STANDARD GAUGE**

HEADQUARTERS
Norchard Railway Centre, Forest Road, Lydney, Gloucestershire, GL15 4FT

PRINCIPAL STATIONS
Norchard Low Level, Lydney Lakeside

HOW TO GET THERE
Road: On B4234 off A48 Chepstow–Gloucester road at Lydney
Bus: Red & White No.73 Chepstow–Gloucester
Rail: Lydney, ¼ mile

☎ Information   01594 843423   Enquiries   01594 845840

TIMES

		Tu Sx					Su Mo
Norchard	Dep	11.00	12.00	13.30	14.20	15.30	16.30
Lydney	Dep	11.25	12.25	13.55	14.45	15.55	16.55

Notes: Tu Sx Tuesdays & Saturdays excepted.
      Su Mo Sundays & Mondays only.

SERVICE OPERATES

Sundays April 9th–September 24th inclusive.
Wednesdays May 31st–August 30th inclusive.
Saturdays in August & Bank Holiday weekend Saturdays.
Tuesdays in August – DMU service only.
Bank Holiday Mondays.
Site open daily Easter–Christmas.

1995 SPECIAL EVENTS

Easter Bunny Hunt	April 14th–17th
VE-Day Celebrations	May 7th/8th
Friends of *Thomas*	June 2nd–4th
	Sept 16th/17th
Modellers Weekend	June 17th/18th
Summer Steam Gala	August 9th–13th
Transport Extravaganza	October 15th
Santa Specials	December (Timings-Aug)

Length of operating line 2 miles

FARES
Adults, £3.50 OAP, £3.00
Children (5-16)   £2.00

6 Steam Locos, 8 Diesels
1995 LOCOS
Pannier 9681, Prairie 5541
Wilbert the Forest Engine.
Services will extend to Lydney Jct
from Easter 1995, subject to DOT
Approval.
BED & BREAKFAST
Treetops   01594 516149
Deanfield   01594 562256

FACILITIES
Souvenir Shop, Footplate Courses, Light Refreshments, Museum, Disabled Facilities,
Car Park, Picnic Site.

Oxon

STANDARD GAUGE

HEAD QUARTERS
> Great Western Society, Didcot, Oxfordshire, OX11 7NJ

HOW TO GET THERE
> Road: A4130 signed from M4 Junction 13
> Bus: Thames Transit 32 01865 772250
>   City of Oxford 37 01865 774611
> Rail: Didcot Parkway (adjacent)

☎ Information 01235 817200

TIMES
> Railway Centre is open every weekend in the year, and daily April 1st to September 24th inclusive.

STEAM DAYS

> First and last Sunday in each month from February–May 28th.
> All Sundays in June, July & August.
> Wednesdays in August only.
> Bank Holidays (not December 25th–28th).

1995 SPECIAL EVENTS

Friends of *Thomas the Tank Engine*	March 3rd–5th September 9th/10th
Children's Steam Day	July 16th
Photographers Evenings	October 27th/28th
Santa Steamings	Suns in December & 23rd/24th

FARES
(Steam Days)
Adults £4.50, Child £3.00
Family £13.50
Prices vary according to event, less for static days.

½ mile demonstration line

22 Steam Locos, 1 Railcar, 1 Shunter

1995 LOCOS
Ex-GWR 1466, 3822, 5029 *Nunney Castle*, 6024 *King Edward 1*, 6998 *Burton Agnes Hall*, 5572 Railcar 22. Visiting *Union of South Africa*. Other Great Western locomotives restored or under restoration.

Didcot is one of the best places to visit for a 'running shed atmosphere'. Plenty of ex-Great Western locos and a short running line for a train ride as well. Excellent museum of GWR artefacts from uniforms to jigsaws!

Former Great Western Railway Engine Shed still fulfilling its intended role.

FACILITIES
Souvenir Shop, Light Refreshments, Full Meals, Museum, Disabled Toilet, Picnic Site, Car Park.

FOREST RAILROAD

MINIMUM GAUGE

HEADQUARTERS
Dobwalls Family Adventure Park, Dobwalls, Nr Liskeard, Cornwall, PL14 6HD
HOW TO GET THERE
Road: off A38 from Plymouth
Bus: National Express Coaches. Ring Plymouth 671121 for details
Rail: Liskeard, 3 miles

☎ Information 01579 20578   Enquiries 01579 20325   Fax 01579 21345

TIMES
Railway runs 10.00–18.00 (last entry 16.30)

DATES
Daily Easter until end of September.
October – weekends only, but daily during Devon & Cornwall half term holidays.
10.00–17.00 (last entries 15.30).

Dobwalls Forest Railway is American Railroading in miniature.

6 Steam Locos and 4 Diesel Locos make up the 7¼" gauge masterpiece, including a replica of a Union Pacific Big Boy 4–8–8–4. Two separate 1 mile long tracks; the Rio Grande Miniature Railroad and The Union Pacific Miniature Railroad. Access to locomotive sheds. Unlimited train rides.

1995 LOCO FLEET
Big Boy, Centennial, Otto Mears, Pioneer, Queen of Wyoming,
Spirit of America, Matthias Baldwin, General Palmer,
Queen of Nebraska, David Curwen.

1995 Admission – not yet decided.

BED & BREAKFAST
J. Wherry   01579 20231

Other attractions within site include shooting gallery, penny arcade,
remote-control trucks, gator boats, aquablasters, and everything to keep children amused whilst you're seriously playing trains.

FACILITIES
Souvenir Shop, Light Refreshments, Full Meals, Edwardian Museum, Disabled Toilet,
Picnic Site, Car Park, Educational Service, Toddlers' Play Area, Woodland Walks.

East Anglian Railway Museum

Essex

HEADQUARTERS
Chappel & Wakes Colne Station, Colchester, Essex, CO6 2DS
PRINCIPAL STATION
Chappel & Wakes Colne
HOW TO GET THERE
Road: Just off A604 Colchester–Cambridge road
Bus: Eastern National 88/88A/88C – Colchester–Halstead route
Rail: Chappel & Wakes Colne (adjacent)

☎ 01206 242524

TIMES
Open every day of the year except December 25th.
Monday to Friday 10.00 to 17.00, weekends & events 10.00 to 17.30.

STEAM DAYS 1995

April 2nd, 14th–17th. May 7th/8th, 28th/29th. June 4th, 18th. July 1st/ 2nd, 23rd.
August 2nd, 6th, 9th, 13th, 16th, 20th, 23rd, 27th/28th, 30th.
September 6th–9th, 30th. October 1st.
December 3rd, 10th, 16th/17th, 24th, 31st.

1995 SPECIAL EVENTS

Victorian Steam	May 7th
VE-Day Anniversary	May 8th.
Teddy Bears' Weekend	May 28th/29th
Father's Day	June 18th.
Model Railways	July1st
Diesel Miscellany & Bus Rally	July 23rd
9th Chappel Beer Festival	September 6th–9th
Santa Specials	December Dates

Length of operating line ⅓ mile

FARES
NORMAL ADMISSION
Adults £2.25, Child/OAP £1.25
Family £6.50
STEAM DAYS (UNLIMITED RIDES)
Adults £4.00, Child/OAP £2.00
Family £11.00

By keeping your entrance ticket on normal Museum day, you may claim discount when returning on Steam Day (except Santas & Beer Festival).

The EARM boasts a heritage/Information Centre that many a bigger attraction would be proud of. Plenty of vintage rolling stock to see in the sheds and the home of the N7.

FACILITIES

Souvenir Shop, Light Refreshments, Full Meals, Museum, Disabled Toilet, Picnic Site, Heritage Centre & Full Educational Service.

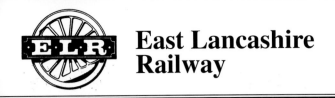

East Lancashire Railway

Lancs

HEADQUARTERS
Bolton Street Station, Bolton Street, Bury, Lancs, BL9 0EY
PRINCIPAL STATIONS
Bury (Bolton Street), Ramsbottom, Rawtenstall
HOW TO GET THERE
Road: M62 Jct 17 (4 miles), M66 Jct 2 (1 mile)
Bus: All bus services to Bury Interchange
Rail: BR Manchester then Metrolink tram to Bury interchange

☎ Enquiries 0161 764 7790 or 01891 517131

TIMES

		S.O D	S A	DA	S A	DA	S A	DA	S A	N D
Bury B.S	Dep	09.00	10.00	11.00	12.00	13.00	14.00	15.00	16.00	17.00
Summerseat	Dep	09.12	10.12	11.12	12.12	13.12	14.12	15.12	16.12	17.12
Ramsbottom	Arr	09.18	10.18	11.18	12.18	13.18	14.18	15.18	16.18	17.18
Ramsbottom	Dep	09.28	10.28	11.28	12.28	13.28	14.28	15.28	16.28	17.28
Irwell Vale	Dep	09.38	10.36	11.36	12.36	13.36	14.36	15.36	16.36	17.36
Rawtenstall	Arr	09.47	10.47	11.47	12.47	13.47	14.47	15.47	16.47	17.47

		S.O D	S A	DA	S A	DA	S A	D	S A	N D
Rawtenstall	Dep	10.00	11.00	12.00	13.00	14.00	15.00	16.00	17.00	18.00
Irwell Vale	Dep	10.08	11.08	12.08	13.08	14.08	15.08	16.08	17.08	18.08
Ramsbottom	Arr	10.17	11.17	12.17	13.17	14.17	15.17	16.17	17.17	18.17
Ramsbottom	Dep	10.25	11.25	12.25	13.25	14.25	15.25	16.25	17.25	18.25
Summerseat	Dep	10.31	11.31	12.31	13.31	14.31	15.31	16.31	17.31	18.31
Bury B.S	Arr	10.42	11.42	12.42	13.42	14.42	15.42	16.42	17.42	18.42

Notes: S.O – Saturdays Only. D – Diesel hauled on Saturdays, Steam on Sundays/ Bank Holidays. S – Steam. N – Not before April 2nd or after September 24th.
A – Midweek Summer steamings from August 7th–25th.

SERVICE OPERATES

Saturdays, Sundays & Bank Holidays until November 26th. Weekdays August 7th–25th

Timetable subject to change on some Special Event days.
A revised timetable will operate from December 2nd.

FARES
Whole Line
Adult Return £6.00, Child £4.00
Rover/Family tickets available

Length of operating line 8 miles

14 Steam Locos, 20 Diesels

WINE & DINE
Irwell Valley Diner, Friday evenings

DRIVING COURSES
Available on Steam or Diesel
Tel 0121 705 8105

1995 SPECIAL EVENTS
Thomas The Tank Engine

Weekend	May 6th–8th
Model Railways	June 3rd/4th
Diesel Week	June 10th–18th
Fire Brigade Display	July 1st/2nd
Transport Extravaganza	July 15th/16th
Services Weekend	August 19th/20th
Teddy Bears' Picnic	August 28th
Diesel Weekend	September 16th/17th

Thomas The Tank Engine

Weekend	Sept 30th–Oct 1st
Steam Gala	October 28th/29th
Santa Specials	December

BED & BREAKFAST
For B&B list, please ring Bury T.I.C. 0161 705 5111

FACILITIES
Souvenir Shop, Light Refreshments, On-Train Buffet, Disabled Toilet, Picnic Site, Car Park, Footplate Courses.

One of our leading steam lines, it's a fair mecca for followers with a diesel persuasion. In a very short time the ELR have established themselves as a force to be reckoned with! Full of good ideas and they haven't finished yet. Scenic views of the west Pennine moors.

Often seen on railtours is No. 4498 *Sir Nigel Gresley*, built at Doncaster in 1937 and based at Steamtown, Carnforth

Eric Sawford

East Somerset Railway

Somerset

The Strawberry Line   STANDARD GAUGE

HEADQUARTERS
> Cranmore Station, Shepton Mallet, Somerset, BA4 4QP

PRINCIPAL STATIONS
> Cranmore, Mendip Vale

HOW TO GET THERE
> Road: 3 miles out of Shepton Mallet on A361
> Bus: Badgerline Services – Frome to Cranmore
> Rail: Frome, 8 miles, Castle Cary, 8 miles

☎ Information 01749 880417 Fax 01749 880764

SITE OPENING TIMES (Cranmore)
Weekends in March, April, October, November, December.
Wednesdays to Sundays May to September.

STEAM OPERATING DATES
Sundays in March and November, weekends April to October, Wednesdays June to
September, Thursdays and Fridays late July to August plus Bank Holidays/events.

1995 SPECIAL EVENTS

Friends of *Thomas*	May 27th–June 4th
Mendip Steam Dream	September 2nd/3rd
David Shepherd's	
Art Exhibition	August 5th/6th
Santa Trains	Weekends in December

9 Steam Locos, 0 Diesels

1995 LOCOS
75029 BR Class 4,
B110 LBSCR E1
STs 705, 1719

FARES
Adults £3.50, Child £2.00
includes unlimited travel

**LINESIDE PHOTOGRAPHIC
PASSES**
£5.00 Non Members

BED & BREAKFAST
01749 880294/880280/880223

ESR – Exclusively Steam Railway! Just Bluebell and East Somerset can currently claim to
have exclusive steam traction. Home for wildlife artist David Shepherd's locos, the engine
shed is pure atmosphere and host to many a jazz night in summer.

FACILITIES

Souvenir Shop, Light Refreshments, Full Meals, Picnic Area, Car Park, Childrens Play Area
Licensed Bar, Museum, Disabled Toilet.

Art Gallery in signal box displaying the work of railway and wildlife artist David Shepherd.
Prints for sale.

N. Yorkshire

'Yorkshire's friendly line'

STANDARD GAUGE

HEADQUARTERS
Embsay Station, Embsay, Nr. Skipton, North Yorkshire, BD23 6AX

PRINCIPAL STATIONS
Embsay, Holywell Halt

HOW TO GET THERE
Road: Signposted from A59 Skipton Bypass
Rail: Skipton, 2 miles

☎ Information & Fax   01756 795189
Enquiries   01756 794727

TIMES

							A
Embsay	Dep	11.00	12.00	13.15	14.15	15.15	16.15

Return trip takes 40 minutes.

SERVICE OPERATES

Steam trains run every Sunday throughout the year, also on Tuesdays & Saturdays in July, then daily (except for Monday & Friday) from July 26th until the end of August.

Also Bank Holidays (except December 25th–26th).

Diesel train service runs on Saturdays in June and September.

Note A: runs March 26th to October 15th.
At peak times, additional trains run to a half hourly timetable.

1995 SPECIAL EVENTS

Mothers Day Special	March 26th
Friends of *Thomas the Tank Engine*	April 14th–17th, May 28th/29th, August 27th/28th.
Summer Funday	July 16th
Steam Gala	September 9th/10th
Halloween Specials	October 29th
Bonfire Night	November 4th
Santa Trains – Sundays Nov 19th to Dec 24th	
Saturdays December 2nd to 16th.	

FARES
Adult £3.00, Child £1.50.

Length of operating line 2½ miles

16 Steam Locos, 8 Diesels

1995 LOCOS
0–6–0 ST's *Wheldale, Primrose,* No. 22, 6118.

WINE & DINE
'The Yorkshire Dalesman' runs on selected evenings.

FACILITIES

Souvenir Shop, Light Refreshments, Full Meals, Bar, On-Train Buffet, Museum, Disabled Access, Picnic Site, Car Park.

Fairbourne Railway   Gwynedd

HEADQUARTERS
Beach Road, Fairbourne, Gwynedd, LL38 2PZ
PRINCIPAL STATIONS
Fairbourne, Porth Penrhyn (Barmouth Ferry)
HOW TO GET THERE
Road: On A493 between Tywyn & Dolgellau
Bus: Service S28 from Barmouth.
Rail: Fairbourne (Cambrian coast line)

☎ Information 01341 250362 Enquiries 01341 250362 Fax 01341 250051

TIMES

Trains depart from Fairbourne
10.45 11.20 11.55 12.30 13.05 13.40 14.30 15.05 15.40 16.15 16.50

Easter weekend, Bank Holidays, Whitsun week, weekends until September.

Length of operating line 2¾ miles

FARES
Adults £3.35, Child £2.05
OAP £2.75
Unlimited travel on day

4 Steam Locos, 1 Diesel
1995 LOCOS
2–6–2T *Yeo*
0–4–0 *Sherpa*

A lovely little beach railway on the Mawddach estuary – minimum gauge at maximum pleasure. The line has had its fair share of troubles over the years but is bouncing back now with its delightful half size replica locos, full signalling and other improvements. Some of the landscape reminds one of the Romney, Hythe & Dymchurch line with its holiday homes, dunes and shingle beaches. The Fairbourne is certainly an historic right of way – the line originated as a 2'0" gauge horse-drawn tramway in 1890.

FACILITIES
Souvenir Shop, Light Refreshments, Full Meals, Bar, Footplate Courses.

Ffestiniog Railway   Gwynedd

NARROW GAUGE

HEADQUARTERS
Harbour Station, Porthmadog, Gwynedd, LL49 9NF

PRINCIPAL STATIONS
Porthmadog, Minffordd, Tan-y-Bwlch, Tan-y-Grisiau, Blaenau Ffestiniog

HOW TO GET THERE
Road: Porthmadog is on the A497
Rail: Porthmadog, Minffordd, Blaenau Ffestiniog

☎ Information 01766 512340
Fax 01766 514576

TIMES – SPRING   Saturday 25th March to Saturday 27th May Except Easter

Mondays – Saturdays

		D				
Pothmadog	Dep	09.45	10.45	12.50	13.50	15.55
Blaenau Ffestiniog	Arr	10.50	11.50	13.55	14.55	17.00
Blaenau Ffestiniog	Dep	11.00	12.05	14.05	15.10	17.15
Porthmadog	Arr	12.10	13.10	15.10	16.15	18.15

Sundays

10.45	11.50	13.50	14.55
11.50	12.50	14.55	16.00
11.05	13.05	15.10	16.10
12.10	14.10	16.15	17.15

EASTER SERVICE   Daily Saturday 15th April to Tuesday 18th April

		D						
Porthmadog	Dep	09.45	10.45	11.50	12.50	13.50	14.55	15.55
Blaenau Ffestiniog	Arr	10.50	11.50	12.50	13.55	14.55	16.00	17.05
Blaenau Ffestiniog	Dep	11.00	12.05	13.05	14.05	15.10	16.10	17.15
Porthmadog	Arr	12.10	13.10	14.10	15.10	16.15	17.15	18.15

(May 6th–8th Special Timetable).

EARLY & LATE SUMMER   Sat 3rd June to Fri 23rd June/Sat 16th September to Sun 24th September
(N.B for Spring Holiday week 28th May to June 2nd see high summer)

Mondays to Saturdays

		D		D		DL
Porthmadog	Dep	09.40	10.45	12.50	13.50	15.55
Blaenau Ffestiniog	Arr	10.45	11.50	13.55	14.55	17.00
Blaenau Ffestiniog	Dep	10.55	12.05	14.05	15.10	17.15
Porthmadog	Arr	12.00	13.10	15.10	16.10	18.15

Sundays

Porthmadog	Dep	10.45	11.50	13.50	14.55
Blaenau Ffestiniog	Arr	11.50	12.50	14.55	16.00
Blaenau Ffestiniog	Dep	12.05	13.05	15.10	16.10
Porthmadog	Arr	13.10	14.10	16.15	17.15

NOTES
D:Diesel Service. DL: Diesel Late Summer.
V:Vintage train.
FO: Fridays Only. SO: Saturdays Only.
Additional shuttle trains operate in the high summer period between Porthmadog & Minfford.
SX: Saturdays excepted.

LOW SUMMER   Sat 24th June to Sat 22nd July/Sat 2nd September to Friday 15th September

Mondays to Thursdays

		D	D					
Porthmadog	Dep	09.40	10.45	11.50	12.50	13.50	14.55	15.55
Blaenau Ffestiniog	Arr	10.45	11.50	13.00	14.00	14.55	16.05	17.05
Blaenau Ffestiniog	Dep	10.55	12.05	13.05	14.05	15.10	16.10	17.15
Porthmadog	Arr	12.10	13.10	14.10	15.10	16.15	17.15	18.15

LOW SUMMER Continued

Fridays & Saturdays

		D				
Porthmadog	Dep	09.40	10.45	12.50	13.50	15.55
Blaenau Ffestiniog	Arr	10.45	11.50	13.55	14.55	17.00
Blaenau Ffestiniog	Dep	10.55	12.05	14.05	15.10	17.15
Porthmadog	Arr	12.00	13.10	15.10	16.10	18.15

Sundays

Porthmadog	Dep	10.45	11.50	12.50	14.55
Blaenau Ffestiniog	Arr	11.50	12.50	14.55	16.00
Blaenau Ffestiniog	Dep	12.05	13.05	15.10	16.10
Porthmadog	Arr	13.10	14.10	16.15	17.15

HIGH SUMMER Sun 23rd July to Fri 1st September (also Spring Bank Holiday 28th May to 2nd Jun)

Mondays to Thursdays

			D								D
Porthmadog	Dep	08.40	09.40	10.45	11.50	12.50	13.50	14.55	15.55	17.00	18.35
Blaenau Ffestiniog	Arr	09.45	10.45	11.55	13.00	14.00	14.55	16.05	17.05	18.10	19.35
Blaenau Ffestiniog	Dep	09.50	10.55	12.05	13.05	14.05	15.10	16.10	17.15	18.35	19.55
Porthmadog	Arr	11.05	12.10	13.10	14.10	15.15	16.15	17.15	18.15	19.40	20.55

Fridays, Saturdays, Sundays

		D							SO V	FO D
Porthmadog	Dep	09.40	10.45	11.50	12.50	13.50	14.55	15.55	17.55	18.35
Blaenau Ffestiniog	Arr	10.45	11.50	13.00	14.00	14.55	16.05	17.05	19.15	19.35
Blaenau Ffestiniog	Dep	10.55	12.05	13.05	14.05	15.10	16.10	17.15	19.55	19.55
Porthmadog	Arr	12.10	13.10	14.10	15.15	16.15	17.15	18.15	20.55	20.55

AUTUMN — Monday 25th September to Friday 20th October

		Mondays to Saturdays				Sundays	
			D		D		
Porthmadog	Dep	10.45	12.50	13.50	15.55	10.45	13.50
Blaenau Ffestiniog	Arr	11.50	13.55	14.55	17.00	11.50	14.55
Blaenau Ffestiniog	Dep	12.05	14.05	15.10	17.15	12.05	15.10
Porthmadog	Arr	13.10	15.10	16.15	18.15	13.10	16.15

Saturday 22nd October to Saturday 29th October

		Mondays to Saturdays					Sundays		Daily 29th Oct to 5th Nov	
		D		D		D				
Porthmadog	Dep	09.40	10.45	12.50	13.50	15.55	10.45	13.50	10.45	13.50
Blaenau Ffestiniog	Arr	10.45	11.50	13.55	14.55	17.00	11.50	14.55	11.50	14.55
Blaenau Ffestiniog	Dep	10.55	12.05	14.05	15.10	17.15	12.05	15.10	12.05	15.10
Porthmadog	Arr	12.00	13.10	15.10	16.10	18.15	13.10	16.15	13.10	16.15

Linking BR's Conway Valley line and the Cambrian Coast route, and now taking tourists instead of slate, the Ffestiniog has some fantastic scenery en-route – sheer drops one side, tunnels, sharp curves, mountainside and lakeside views – even a spiral.

1995 SPECIAL EVENT
Steam Gala '95   May 6th–8th

Length of operating line 13½ miles

13 Steam Locos, 4 Diesels

FACILITIES
Souvenir Shop, Light Refreshments, Full Meals, Licensed Bar, On-Train Buffet, Museum, Disabled Toilet, Picnic Site, Car Park.

Foxfield Railway

Staffs

HEADQUARTERS
> Blythe Bridge (Caverswall Road) Station, Stoke-on-Trent, Staffordshire, ST11 9EA

PRINCIPAL STATIONS
> Blythe Bridge (Caverswall Road), Dilhorne Park

HOW TO GET THERE
> Road: A50/A521 south of Stoke
> Bus: Staffordshire Bus. Tel 01785 223344
> Rail: Blythe Bridge, ½ mile

☎ Weekdays 01782 396210   Weekends 01270 874959

TIMES

Blythe Bridge (Caverswall Road) Dep	11.30	13.00	14.00	15.00	16.00
Dilhorne Park Arr	11.50	13.20	14.20	15.20	16.20
Dilhorne Park Dep	12.00	13.30	14.30	15.30	16.30
Blythe Bridge (Caverswall Road) Arr	12.20	13.50	14.50	15.50	16.50

SERVICE OPERATES
> Sundays Easter to end of September, plus Bank Holiday Sats/Mons. On Special Event days, a more frequent service may operate.

FARES (to be revised)

Adults	£3.00
Children/OAP	£1.50
Family (2 Adults & 2 Children)	£8.00

All are Day Rovers except Special Event Days.

Length of operating line 2½ miles

14 Steam Locos, 12 Diesels

1995 LOCOS
*Whiston, No. 11,
Wimblebury, Little Barford*

This line is famous in railway circles for its 1 in 19 gradient on Dilhorne Bank. The Barclays, Bagnalls and Pecketts are perfectly at home on the former colliery line. A picturesque line and charming 'buffet car' with veranda – now that's style!

FACILITIES
Souvenir Shop, Light Refreshments, Bar, Museum, Car Park, Disabled Coach, Footplate Courses.

Gloucestershire

GLOUCESTERSHIRE WARWICKSHIRE RAILWAY
– THE FRIENDLY LINE IN THE COTSWOLDS –

STANDARD GAUGE

HEADQUARTERS
The Station, Toddington, Nr Winchcombe, Gloucestershire, GL54 5DT

PRINCIPAL STATIONS
Toddington, Winchcombe

HOW TO GET THERE
Road: Junction of B4632/B4077, 8 miles from Jct 9, M5
Bus: Castleways Services. Tel 01242 602949
Rail: Cheltenham Spa, 9 miles

☎ Information 01242 621405

TIMES
Toddington   Dep 11.00 and frequent intervals until 16.50.
Weekends and Bank Holidays from March until September 10th.
Then Sundays until end of November.
Whitsun week and school holidays.

1995 SPECIAL EVENTS
Steam & Diesel Gala   March 18th/19th
VE-Day   May 8th
Thomas & Friends   June 24th/25th
Transport Gala   July 2nd
Teddy Bears' Picnic   August 5th/6th
Diesel Week   August 7th–12th
                        (not Wed)

30th Anniversary of
BR closure   September 3rd
Steam & Vintage Gala   October 14th/15th
Diesel Gala   November 11th/12th

WINE & DINE
'Moonlight Express' – evenings, please phone

FARES
Adults   £5.00
Child/OAP   £3.00

Length of operating line 5 miles

6 Steam Locos, 8 Diesels
1995 LOCOS
GWR 2–6–2T 4566
visiting engines for galas

PHOTOGRAPHIC PASSES
Members £10, Non Members £20
per annum.

BED & BREAKFAST
Rosebay 01242 602438
Cleveley 01242 602059

The GWR have had a fine visiting line-up of GWR locos in the past, including *Defiant* and *City of Truro*. This line has recently made considerable progress and eventually hope to rebuild to Cheltenham. The line used to provide a direct route from Birmingham to Cheltenham via Stratford-upon-Avon. Don't forget to see the 2'0" gauge line at Toddington.

FACILITIES

Souvenir Shop, Light Refreshments, On-Train Buffet, Disabled Facilities, Car Park, Footplate Courses, 2'0" Gauge Railway.

GORSE BLOSSOM
RAILWAY

Devon

MINIMUM GAUGE

HEADQUARTERS
> Bickington, Newton Abbot, Devon, TQ12 6JD

PRINCIPAL STATION
> Wellpark Central

HOW TO GET THERE
> Road: Off old A38 between Drumbridges roundabout (A38/A382) and Bickington (A38/A383) between Chudleigh–Ashburton
>
> Bus: Devon General x38/39 Exeter–Plymouth
> 72, 173 from Newton Abbott. Tel 01392 382800
>
> Rail: Newton Abbot, 5 miles

☎ Information 01626 821361

TIMES

> * 10.30, 11.00, then every 20 minutes (except 13.00) to 16.40.
> Last admission to park 16.00.

SERVICE OPERATES

> Daily April 9th to October 8th.
> Extra Train at 10.40* operates school holidays, Bank Holidays, but not Saturdays.
> (Easter, Whitsun and July 24th–September 5th inclusive.)
>
> *Woodland Express – 1½ mile non-stop run.

FARES

Length of operating line ¾ mile

Admission to park, and includes
unlimited train rides

1995 LOCOS
Lynton & Barnstaple 2–6–2T *Yeo* (⅓ full size)
Rhaetian Railway Ge 4/4 II No. 615 *Klosters*
(⅛ full size)
Battery Electric Loco

Adults	£3.50
Child	£2.50
OAP	£3.00

This 7¼" gauge line is part of a woodland park, overlooking the Teign valley with views from Dartmoor to Haldon, bordering the National Park.

FACILITIES
Souvenir Shop, Light Refreshments, Full Meals, Disabled Toilet, Picnic Site, Car Park, Children's Play Village, Nature Trails, Swiss Garden Model Railway.

Leicestershire

HEADQUARTERS
> Loughborough Central Station, Great Central Road, Loughborough, Leicestershire, LE11 1RW

PRINCIPAL STATIONS
> Loughborough Ctl, Quorn & Woodhouse, Rothley, Leicester North

HOW TO GET THERE
> Road: Loughborough Central is off A6 south of town centre
>   Leicester North is adjacent to Leicester Ring Road
> Bus: Leicester Local Services
> Rail: Loughborough (Midland), 10 mins walk

☎ Information 01509 230726 Enquiries 01509 230726 Fax 01509 239791

TIMES

TABLE A

		B	A	B	A	B	A	B	C
Loughborough	Dep	10.00	10.45	12.00	13.18	14.30	15.15	16.30	17.05
Quorn	Dep	-- --	10.53	12.08	13.23	14.38	15.23	16.38	17.13
Rothley	Arr	-- --	11.01	12.16	13.31	14.46	15.31	16.46	17.21
Rothley	Dep	-- --	11.03	12.18	13.33	14.48	15.33	16.48	17.27
Leicseter North	Arr	10.22	11.12	12.27	13.42	14.57	15.42	16.57	17.35
Leicester North	Dep	10.45	11.25	12.40	13.55	15.15	15.55	17.15	17.50
Rothley	Arr	10.56	11.35	12.50	14.05	15.25	16.05	17.25	18.00
Rothley	Dep	11.04	11.37	12.52	14.07	15.32	16.07	17.27	18.01
Quorn	Dep	11.12	11.45	13.00	14.15	15.40	16.15	17.34	18.09
Loughborough	Arr	11.19	11.52	13.07	14.22	15.47	16.22	17.41	18.15

A TRAINS OPERATE on Saturdays, Sundays & Bank Holiday Mondays throughout the year. and DAILY from April 18th–21st and from May 1st–September 29th.

B TRAINS OPERATE on Saturdays, Sundays & Bank Holiday Mondays throughout the year.

C SEASONAL SERVICE – Saturdays only from April 1st–October 28th.

TABLE B (Evenings Only)

		D	E	D
Loughborough	Dep	18.20	19.30	20.05
Quorn	Dep	18.28	-- --	20.13
Rothley	Arr	18.36	20.04	20.32
Rothley	Dep	18.38	20.06	20.42
Leicester North	Arr	18.45	20.15	20.51
Leicester North	Dep	19.00	20.30	21.06
Rothley	Arr	19.10	20.40	21.15
Rothley	Dep	19.11	21.10	21.26
Quorn	Dep	19.19	-- --	21.34
Loughborough	Arr	19.25	21.25	21.40

D TRAINS OPERATE on Saturdays only from May 6th–September 2nd and are DMU operated.

E 'Charnwood Forester' dining train – most Saturday evenings. Advance booking required. Additional trains run during Gala Days & Bank Holiday Mondays, also November 25th until December 31st, when a special timetable is in operation.

1995 SPECIAL EVENTS

Western Locos Weekend	March 11th/12th
Diesel Weekend	March 31st–April 2nd
Road-Rail Steam Rally & Bulleid Locos Weekend	April 14th–17th
VE-Day/Wartime Weekend	May 6th–8th
Summer Steam Gala	June 24th/25th
Thomas Week	July 29th–August 6th
Autumn Gala	September 16th/17th
Mixed Traffic – Steam & Diesel Gala	October 7th/8th
Thomas Weekend	October 21st/22nd
Bonfire Night	November 4th
Santa Specials	November 25th/26th & December Weekends

FARES

Round Trip – starting at any station
Adults £6.00, Child/OAP £4.00
Family £15.00
Fares due to be reviewed

Length of operating line 8 miles

20 Steam Locos, 4 Diesels

1995 LOCOS
5593, *Kolhapur*, 5231, 34039, 34101, 35005, 69523

WINE & DINE
Silver Jubilee (Sat/Sun lunch)
Carillion, Master Cutler (Weds)
Charnwood Forester (Sat Eves)

LINESIDE PHOTO PASSES
£10 members, £20 Non-Members

BED & BREAKFAST
Great Central Hotel
01509 263405
Kings Head Hotel
01509 214893

Now in the top league of Independent railways, the GCR are going for 'main line experience' in the doubling of track sections. A splendid pool of ex-mainline locos ready for a further extension, this time northwards, to the southern tip of Nottingham. A true InterCity line in the making.

FACILITIES
Souvenir Shop, Light Refreshments, On-Train Buffet, Museum, Picnic Sites, Car Park, Footplate Courses, Disabled Toilet on train, Full Meals.

DISCOVER BRITAIN'S ONLY PRESERVED MAIN LINE STEAM RAILWAY

Step back in time to the glorious days of *Main Line* steam travel at *Leicestershire's Great Central Railway*.

Discover *restored period stations*, working *signal boxes*, a *Museum* and the heaviest and most impressive *British steam locomotives*.

Relax with a sumptous **6 course meal** on one of our regular *dining trains*, or simply watch the world go by from the comfort of your carriage.

It's a great way to make everyone's day, *every day* from *May to September* and *every weekend* and *Bank Holiday Monday* throughout the year.

 GREAT CENTRAL RAILWAY
Loughborough • Quorn • Rothley • Leicester
A great way to make everyone's day

FOR MORE INFORMATION RING 01509 230726

Fresh from a complete overhaul, the National Railway Museum's No. 46229 *Duchess of Hamilton* is seen visiting the Great Central Railway in August 1994

Eric Sawford

Snowdon Mountain Railway No. 8 *Eryi* at Summit Station

Eric Sawford

Isle of Man

HEADQUARTERS
    Groudle Glen, Onchan, Isle of Man
    Postal Address: 19 Ballabrooie Grove, Douglas, Isle of Man, IM1 4ET

NARROW GAUGE

PRINCIPAL STATION
    Lhen Coan

HOW TO GET THERE
    Road: 2 miles from Douglas on coast road to Laxey
    Rail: Manx Electric Railway stops at Groudle Hotel

☎ 01624 622138 evenings only; 01624 670453 weekends only

TIMES
    Regular departures from Lhen Coan to Headland between 11.00 and 16.30.
    Evening service runs between 19.00 and 21.00 Wednesdays in July & August.

SERVICE OPERATES
    April 16th/17th, Sundays from April 30th–October 1st. August 21st–26th.*
    Bank Holiday Mondays May 8th, May 29th, August 29th.
    Wednesday evenings July 5th–August 23rd.

1995 SPECIAL EVENTS – In conjunction with Isle of Man Railways
* Snaefell Mountain Railway Centenary Week   August 21st–26th.

FARES Adult £1.40, Child 70p

Length of operating line ¾ mile

FACILITIES Souvenir Shop, Picnic Site, Car Park.

2 Steam Locos, 2 Diesels

ISLE OF
M A N

Select with

TRAVEL SERVICES

ISLE OF MAN

SNAEFELL CENTENARY
CELEBRATIONS 1995

3 nights By Air from £133 p/p
(Incl. Return flight from Liverpool or Blackpool Airports
(Free Parking), B & B & 3 Day Rover Ticket)

3 nights By Sea from £106 p/p
(Incl. Return Ferry from Heysham, B & B & 3 Day Rover Ticket)

For more information, telephone or write to:
TRAVEL SERVICES (IOM)
Harris Promenade, Douglas, Isle of Man, IM1 2RN.
ABTA 7496 **Telephone: (01624) 661177 Fax: (01624) 661667** ATOL 1965

Gwili Railway   Dyfed

STANDARD GAUGE

HEADQUARTERS
Bronwydd Arms Station, Bronwydd, Carmarthen, Dyfed, SA33 6HT.
PRINCIPAL STATIONS
Bronwydd Arms, Llwyfan Cerrig
HOW TO GET THERE
Road: On A484 3 miles north of Carmarthen
Rail: Carmarthen, 3 miles

☎   Information   01267 230666

TIMES

							W	
Bronwydd Arms	Dep	11.00	12.00	13.30	14.30	15.30	16.30

W: Not Wednesdays in May or October 22nd & 25th.

Bank Holiday Mondays – trains start 10.30 and every
45 minutes until 17.15.
June 10th/11th – Special Service.

DECEMBER ONLY: 11.00 and every 45 minutes until 14.45

SERVICE OPERATES
April 14th–19th, 23rd & 30th. May 3rd, 7th/8th, 10th, 14th, 17th, 21st, 24th, 28th–31st.
June 1st–4th, 7th, 10th/11th, 14th, 18th, 21st, 23rd, 25th, 28th.
July 1st/2nd, 5th, 9th, 12th, 16th, 19th, 22nd–31st.
August – Daily.
September 1st–3rd, 10th, 17th, 24th.
October 22nd, 25th.
December 3rd, 9th/10th, 16th/17th, 23rd/24th.

1995 SPECIAL EVENTS		**FARES**		**1995 LOCOS**
		Adult Return	£2.80	incl. Welsh Guardsman,
Easter Egg Hunt	April 14th/15th	Children 5–16,		Rosyth No. 1, *Olwen* .
Big Kids' Day	May 14th	OAP, UB40	£1.40	
Gala Weekend	June 10th/11th	Family	£7.20	
Teddy Bear Weekend	July 1st/2nd			7 Steam Locos, 7 Diesels
Santa Specials	December			

This ex-Great Western line's society intends to
eventually restore services from Llanpumpsaint
to Abergwili.

Length of operating line 1.6 miles
Steam-operated 7.25" gauge
miniature line.

FACILITIES
Souvenir Shop, Light Refreshments, On-Train Buffet, Car Park, Picnic Site,
Footplate Courses, Disabled Coach, Photographic Passes.

Heatherslaw Light Railway Northumberland

HEADQUARTERS

Ford Forge, Heatherslaw, Cornhill-on-Tweed, Northumberland, TD12 4QA

PRINCIPAL STATIONS

Heatherslaw, Etal Castle

HOW TO GET THERE

Road: A1 or A69 to B6354

Rail: Berwick, 10 miles

☎ Information   01890 820 244/317

TIMES

Hourly service from 10.30 to 15.30

SERVICE OPERATES

Daily from Easter until end of October.

In high season and Bank Holidays, additional trains may run – diesel hauled.

1995 SPECIAL EVENTS

Good Friday

Activity Day   April 14th

Teddy Bears' Picnic   September 2nd

Santa Specials   December 9th/10th

                        16th/17th, 22nd/23rd

BED & BREAKFAST

Hay farm, Ford Fountain, Coach House.
Please telephone railway for full details.

FARES

Adults	£3.00
Children	£1.50
Infants (under 5s)	£0.75
OAP	£2.25

First Train of the Day (10.30)
Children in charge, bring your parents,
all travel for £1.50 each.

Length of operating line 1¾ miles

1 Steam Loco, 1 Diesel

The Heatherslaw estate includes a water mill, riverside cafe, and working blacksmiths and woodturning shop at the Errol Hut Smithy.

15" gauge loco *Lady Augusta* is reputed to be the only steam engine in the world with disc brakes for additional safety.

FACILITIES

Souvenir Shop, Light Refreshments, Full Meals, Railway Room with OO gauge layout, Disabled Facilities, Picnic Site, Car Park.

Schools service – guided educational talk.

NOSTALGIC STEAM DAYS OUT

THE BRISTOLIAN

THE CUMBRIAN MOUNTAIN EXPRESS

THE COTSWOLD VENTURER

THE STRONG COUNTRYMAN

THE TORBAY LIMITED

THE WELSH MARCHES EXPRESS

Telephone for Information and Bookings
01543 419472
(09.00 -17.00 Monday to Friday, continuous to 21.00 Weds only)
or write to:
WATERMAN RAILWAYS
P.O. Box 4472, Lichfield, Staffs. WS13 6RU
Fax: 01543 250817

Heritage Days Out
(Steam hauled tours on the main line)   1995 TOURS

THE BRISTOLIAN
Steam haulage throughout the entire trip.Leaving Paddington around 08.45,picking up at Slough,Reading,Didcot and Swindon.Optional tour to SS *Great Britain* during stay in Bristol. Planned locos 5029 *Nunney Castle*,35028 *Clan Line*,70000 *Britannia* and 71000 *Duke of Gloucester*. Operating dates June 4th,July 2nd,30th.August 27th.September 24th.

THE CUMBRIAN MOUNTAIN EXPRESS
Forever linked with the Settle and Carlisle route,steam over the viaducts and up the gradients on the backbone of England.Allocated locos 46229 *Duchess of Hamilton*,71000 *Duke of Gloucester*,46203 *Princess Margaret Rose*.
Operating dates June 3rd,10th.July 8th,22nd.August 5th,19th.September 2nd,16th.

THE COTSWOLD VENTURER
Steam through the Cotswolds between Didcot and Kidderminster via Moreton-in-Marsh,Worcester and Cheltenham,Kemble and Swindon on the return leg.Explore Elgar country or Severn Valley Railway.Planned locos 30777 *Sir Lamiel*,5029 *Nunney Castle*,70000 *Britannia*.
Operating dates June 17th.July 15th.August 12th.September 9th,30th.

THE STRONG COUNTRYMAN
From that famous old ad slogan 'You are now entering Strong Country'.To the Dorset coast via Brockenhurst for New Forest or Beaulieu Motor Museum.Planned locos 35028 *Clan Line*,30777 *Sir Lamiel*,70000 *Britannia*.
Operating dates June 11th.July 9th,23rd.August 6th,20th.September 3rd,17th.

THE TORBAY LIMITED
Entirely steam journey from Bristol Temple Meads to Paignton! Proposed locos 7825 and 7802 *Bradley Manor*.
Operating dates May 29th.June 4th,7th,11th,14th,18th,21st,25th,28th.
July 2nd,5th,9th,12th,16th,19th,20th,23rd,26th,27th,30th.
August 2nd,3rd,6th,9th,10th,13th,16th,17th,20th,23rd, 24th,27th,28th,30th,31st.
September 3rd,6th.

THE WELSH MARCHES EXPRESS
Steam haulage in either direction between Worcester and Crewe,passing through Gloucester,Newport,Hereford and Shrewsbury.Planned locos 46203 *Princess Margaret Rose*,71000 *Duke of Gloucester*.
Operating dates July1st,29th.August 26th.September 23rd.

Average fares for above tours from £38.00 Standard class.

In April and May 1995,steam hauled tours consist of a variety of departure and destination points.Enquire for full details.

Also POSITIONING TRAINS – tours at special low prices.

For full details of the above and additional pick-up stations en-route,contact:
Waterman Railways,PO Box 4472,Lichfield,Staffs WS13 6RU. Tel 01543 419472.

Isle of Man Steam Railway

Isle of Man

HEADQUARTERS

Isle of Man Steam Railway, Isle of Man Railways, Strathallan Crescent,
Douglas, Isle of Man, IM2 4NR

PRINCIPAL STATIONS

Douglas, Port Soderick, Ballasalla, Castletown, Colby, Port St. Mary, Port Erin

HOW TO GET THERE

Sea: From Heysham, Liverpool, Dublin, Belfast. (I.O.M Steam Packet)
Air: Manx Airlines from Birmingham, Cardiff, Dublin, Glasgow,
Jersey, Liverpool, London Heathrow/Luton, Manchester, Southampton,
(Belfast, Blackpool, Cork, Leeds, Newcastle – summer service)
Road: Car ferry from Liverpool or Heysham
Rail: To Heysham, via Lancaster/Preston/Manchester (Euston 10.00)
Bus: I.O.M Transport Services, connect at Douglas station

☎ Information & Enquiries   01624 663366   Fax   01624 663637

TIMES

TABLE A

Douglas	Dep	10.10	11.45	14.10	16.10	Port Erin	Dep	10.15	12.05	14.15	16.15
Port Soderick	Dep	10.23	11.58	14.23	16.23	Port St Mary	Dep	10.19	12.09	14.19	16.19
Ballasalla	Dep	10.45	12.20	14.45	16.45	Colby	Dep	10.27	12.17	14.27	16.27
Castletown	Dep	10.52	12.28	14.52	16.52	Castletown	Dep	10.38	12.28	14.38	16.38
Colby	Dep	11.03	12.38	15.03	17.03	Ballasalla	Dep	10.45	12.35	14.45	16.45
Port St Mary	Dep	11.12	12.47	15.12	17.12	Port Soderick	Dep	11.07	12.55	15.07	17.07
Port Erin	Arr	11.15	12.50	15.15	17.15	Douglas	Arr	11.20	13.10	15.20	17.20

TABLE A OPERATES

Daily April 14th to July 2nd & September 1st to October 1st & October 21st–29th.
Also Fridays, Saturdays & Sundays between July 7th & August 27th.

TABLE B

Douglas	Dep	10.10	10.50	11.45	14.10	15.55	16.55
Port Soderick	Dep	10.23	11.08	11.58	14.23	16.08	17.08
Ballasalla	Dep	10.45	11.30	12.20	14.45	16.30	17.30
Castletown	Dep	10.52	11.37	12.28	14.52	16.37	17.37
Colby	Dep	11.03	11.48	12.38	15.03	16.48	17.48
Port St Mary	Dep	11.12	11.57	12.47	15.12	16.57	17.57
Port Erin	Arr	11.15	12.00	12.50	15.15	17.00	18.00
Port Erin	Dep	10.15	12.05	14.15	15.15	16.15	17.15
Port St Mary	Dep	10.19	12.09	14.19	15.19	16.19	17.19
Colby	Dep	10.27	12.17	14.27	15.27	16.27	17.27
Castletown	Dep	10.38	12.28	14.38	15.38	16.38	17.38
Ballasalla	Dep	10.45	12.35	14.45	15.45	16.45	17.45
Port Soderick	Dep	11.07	12.55	15.07	16.07	17.07	18.07
Douglas	Arr	11.20	13.10	15.20	16.20	17.20	18.20

TABLE B OPERATES

Mondays to Thursdays only from July 3rd to August 31st.
For Fridays, Saturdays & Sundays in this period see Table A.

FARES
Full Line Return
Adults £6.20, Child 5-15 Half Fare
Adult 1 Day Rover £8.80
      3 Day Rover £13.00
7 Day Island Freedom £24.00 (prov)

1995 LOCOS
No. 4 *Loch*, No. 10 *G.H. Wood*,
No. 11 *Maitland*, No. 12 *Hutchinson*
No. 15 *Caledonia*

Many special offers are in operation to enable the visitor to travel on the Manx Electric Railway (tramcars), Douglas horse trams, and Isle of Man Buses, in conjunction with the Steam Railway (see also page 53).

At 15 ⅜ miles in length, the Isle of Man Steam Railway is the longest narrow gauge line in the British Isles. The island's Victorian transport systems are a mecca for enthusiasts around the globe.

Workshop visits can be arranged for special parties and schools. Trains can be hired, and Isle of Man Railways offer footplate courses with a difference by offering 'Motorman' lessons to drive an electric tram on the Manx Electric Railway.

FACILITIES

Souvenir Shop, Light Refreshments, Full Meals, Museum (Port Erin), Disabled Facilities, Car Park,Special Offers within Isle of Man Transport. B&B guide from Dept. of Tourism (01624) 686766

ISLE OF MAN INTERNATIONAL RAILWAY FESTIVAL – 1995

In conjunction with the Centenary in 1995 of the electrically-worked Snaefell Mountain Railway it is planned to steam No. 15 *Caledonia* (the locomotive engaged on construction of the line in 1895) on the Snaefell Mountain Railway on the following dates:

April 29th/30th, May 7th/8th, June 24th–26th, August 22nd/23rd, 25th–27th, September 23rd/24th & 30th, October 1st (all provisional dates).

Provisional dates for steam on the Manx Electric Railway are April 15th–17th, May 5th/6th (No.4 *Loch*) and August 16th–19th (No.15 *Caledonia*)

SPECIAL EVENTS 1995

International Railway Festival Launch	April 14th–17th
Enthusiasts' Week	April 29th–May 8th
Vintage Rally & Steam Gala Week	June 24th–July 1st
Centenary Fortnight	August 12th–26th
Festival Finale Week	September 23rd–October 1st

ISLE OF MAN INTERNATIONAL RAILWAY FESTIVAL

FEBRUARY 8th
Snaefell Mountain Railway Stamp Issue

APRIL 14th - 17th
International Railway Festival Launch

APRIL 29th - MAY 8th
Enthusiasts Week

JUNE 24th - JULY 1st
Vintage Rally and Steam Gala Week

AUGUST 11th - 13th
Family Jamboree Weekend

AUGUST 12th - 26th
Centenary Fortnight

AUGUST 25th - 28th
Centenary Jazz Festival

SEPTEMBER 23rd - OCTOBER 1st
Festival Finale Week

For a full programme of each events period contact:
Isle of Man Railways
Strathallan Crescent Douglas
Isle of Man   IM2 4NR   Tel. 01624 663366

Isle of Wight

STANDARD GAUGE

HEADQUARTERS
The Railway Station, Havenstreet, Isle of Wight, PO33 4DS

PRINCIPAL STATIONS
Smallbrook Junction, Havenstreet, Wootton

HOW TO GET THERE
Road: via Havenstreet village, 3 miles SW of Ryde
Bus: Southern Vectis 1a to Wootton Station (approx ½ hourly from Ryde)
Rail: Smallbrook Junction, direct interchange with BR Island line.
         No road access to Smallbrook Junction or Ashey

☎ Information 01983 884343   Enquires 01983 882204   Fax   01983 884515

TIMES

Smallbrook Jct.	Dep	-- --	10.25	11.25	12.25	13.41	14.41	15.41	16.41	
Ashey (request)	Dep	-- --	-- --	-- --	-- --	-- --	-- --	-- --	-- --	
Havenstreet	Arr	-- --	10.36	11.36	12.36	13.52	14.52	15.52	16.52	
Havenstreet	Dep	-- --	10.40	11.40	12.40	13.56	14.56	15.56	16.53+	
Wootton	Arr	-- --	10.45	11.45	12.45	14.01	15.01	16.01	16.58+	
Wootton	Dep	-- --	10.55	11.55	12.50	14.11	15.11	16.11	17.03+	
Havenstreet	Arr	-- --	11.00	12.00	12.55	14.16	15.16	16.16	17.08+	
Havenstreet	Dep	10.05	11.07	12.07	13.23	14.23	15.23	16.23	-- --	
Ashey (request)	Dep	-- --	-- --	-- --	-- --	-- --	-- --	-- --	-- --	
Smallbrook Jct.	Arr	10.16	11.18	12.18	13.34	14.34	15.34	16.34	-- --	

+ Does not run October 22nd & 26th

SERVICE OPERATES

March 23rd, 26th, 30th. April 2nd, 6th, 9th, 13th/14th, 16th/17th, 20th, 23rd, 26th, 27th, 30th.
May 3rd/4th, 7th/8th, 10th/11th, 14th, 17th/18th, 21st, 24th/25th, 28th–31st.
June-Daily except Mondays, Fridays, Saturdays.
July 2nd, 4th–6th, 9th, 11th–13th, 16th, 18th–20th, 23rd–31st. August-Daily.
September 1st–3rd, 5th–7th, 10th, 12th–14th, 17th, 19th–21st, 24th, 26th–28th.
October – Sundays & Thurdays only. (Special timetable operates October 29th.)
December 17th, 23rd/24th, 26th.

FARES (full line – unlimited travel-day)
Adults £6.50,
Child £4.00
Family £18.00
(2 Adults, and 4 Children)

BED & BREAKFAST
I of W T.I.C. 01983 524 343

Length of operating line 5 miles

6 Steam Locos, 3 Diesels
1995 LOCOS: *Calbourne, Freshwater, Newport, Royal Engineer*

PHOTOGRAPHIC PASSES
Members & Non Members £5 (day)

Perfectly preserving the unique atmosphere of the Southern Railway's presence on the I.O.W. Pre-grouping engines and coaches, and ex-LT stock to get you to Smallbrook.

FACILITIES Souvenir Shop, Light Refreshments, Museum, Disabled Toilet, Picnic Site, Car Park.

W. Yorkshire

KEIGHLEY & WORTH VALLEY RAILWAY   **STANDARD GAUGE**

HEADQUARTERS
Haworth Station, Haworth, Nr Keighley, West Yorkshire, BD22 8NJ
PRINCIPAL STATIONS
Keighley, Ingrow West, Oakworth, Haworth, Oxenhope
HOW TO GET THERE
Road: Off A629 Keighley/Halifax road
Bus: Leeds or Bradford to Keighley or Haworth
Rail: Keighley (shared station)
Through bookings available to Oxenhope (Worth Valley) from any BR Travel Centre

☎ Information 01535 647777 Enquiries 01535 645214 Fax 01535 647317

TIMES
TABLE A

		D	D					
Oxenhope	Dep	09.20	10.35	11.10	12.30	13.50	15.20	16.45
Haworth	Dep	09.26	10.40	11.16	12.36	13.56	15.26	16.51
Oakworth	Dep	09.29	10.43	11.19	12.39	13.59	15.29	16.54
Damems	R	09.34	10.48	11.24	12.44	14.04	15.34	16.59
Ingrow(West)	Dep	09.38	10.50	11.29	12.49	14.09	15.39	17.04
Keighley	Arr	09.45	10.55	11.35	12.55	14.15	15.45	17.10
		D	D					
Keighley	Dep	10.05	11.15	11.50	13.10	14.35	16.05	17.25
Ingrow(West)	Dep	10.09	11.19	11.56	13.16	14.41	16.11	17.31
Damems	R	10.11	11.21	11.59	13.19	14.44	16.14	17.34
Oakworth	Dep	10.15	11.25	12.04	13.24	14.50	16.20	17.40
Haworth	Dep	10.20	11.30	12.09	13.29	14.54	16.24	17.44
Oxenhope	Arr	10.26	11.36	12.15	13.35	15.00	16.30	17.50

TABLE B

Oxenhope	Dep	11.20	12.45	14.20	15.50
Haworth	Dep	11.26	12.51	14.26	15.56
Oakworth	Dep	11.29	12.54	14.29	15.59
Damems	R	11.32	12.57	14.32	16.02
Ingrow(West)	Dep	11.35	13.00	14.35	16.05
Keighley	Arr	11.45	13.10	14.45	16.15
Keighley	Dep	12.05	13.35	15.05	16.35
Ingrow(West)	Dep	12.10	13.40	15.10	16.40
Damems	R	12.11	13.41	15.11	16.41
Oakworth	Dep	12.16	13.46	15.16	16.46
Haworth	Dep	12.23	13.53	15.23	16.53
Oxenhope	Arr	12.30	14.00	15.30	17.00

NOTES:
D: Diesel Heritage Traction   R: Request Stop

TABLE A OPERATES
SATURDAYS March 4th to February 24th 1996 except April 15th & December 30th. Special Event Saturdays and pre-Christmas Saturdays.
SPRING & AUTUMN SUNDAYS
March 5th, 12th, 19th, 26th
April 9th, 23rd, 30th. May 14th.
June 18th, 25th.
October 8th, 15th, 22nd, 29th.

TABLE B OPERATES
SPRING & SUMMER MIDWEEK
WINTER SUNDAYS/XMAS HOLIDAYS
April 19th–21st, May 30th–June 2nd,
Weekdays June 19th–September 1st
except August 28th.
November Sundays, and December 26th to January 1st 1996.
Sundays January 7th–February 26th 1996.

TABLE C

		D	D		D									
Oxenhope	Dep	09.20	10.25	11.00	11.45	12.30	13.15	14.00	14.45	15.30	16.15	17.00	17.45	
Haworth	Dep	09.26	10.30	11.07	11.56	12.37	13.22	14.07	14.52	15.37	16.22	17.07	17.52	
Oakworth	Dep	09.29	10.33	11.11	11.59	12.41	13.26	14.11	14.56	15.41	16.26	17.11	17.56	
Damems	R	09.32	10.36	11.15	12.03	12.45	13.30	14.15	15.00	15.45	16.30	17.15	18.00	
Ingrow	Dep	09.36	10.40	11.19	12.06	12.49	13.34	14.19	15.04	15.49	16.34	17.19	18.04	
Keighley	Arr	09.45	10.45	11.25	12.11	12.55	13.40	14.25	15.10	15.55	16.40	17.25	18.10	
Keighley	Dep	09.55	11.05	11.50	12.30	13.15	14.00	14.45	15.30	16.15	17.00	17.45	18.30	
Ingrow	Dep	09.59	11.09	11.56	12.35	13.21	14.06	14.51	15.36	16.21	17.06	17.51	18.35	
Damems	R	10.01	11.12	11.59	12.38	13.25	14.10	14.55	15.40	16.25	17.10	17.55	18.38	
Oakworth	Dep	10.05	11.19	12.05	12.47	13.32	14.17	15.02	15.47	16.32	17.17	18.02	18.48	
Haworth	Dep	10.10	11.24	12.10	12.50a	13.37	14.22	15.07	15.52	16.37	17.22	18.07	18.53	
Oxenhope	Arr	10.16	11.30	12.17	-- --	13.42	14.27	15.12	15.57	16.42	17.27	18.12	18.58	

TABLE C OPERATES
SUMMER SUNDAYS & BANK HOLIDAYS
April 14th–18th. May 7th/8th, 28th/29th. August 28th.
Sundays July 9th to September 24th except August 13th.

TABLE D

		D	D	D	D	D	D	D
Oxenhope	Dep	10.30	11.30	12.30	13.30	14.30	15.30	16.30
Haworth	Dep	10.35	11.35	12.35	13.33a	14.35	15.35	16.35
Oakworth	Dep	10.38	11.38	12.38	-- --	14.38	15.38	16.38
Damems	R	10.41	11.41	12.41	-- --	14.41	15.41	16.41
Ingrow	Dep	10.43	11.43	12.43	-- --	14.43	15.43	16.43
Keighley	Arr	10.48	11.48	12.48	-- --	14.48	15.48	16.48
Keighley	Dep	11.05	12.05	13.05	-- --	15.05	16.05	17.05
Ingrow	Dep	11.09	12.09	13.09	-- --	15.09	16.09	17.09
Damems	R	11.11	12.11	13.11	-- --	15.11	16.11	17.11
Oakworth	Dep	11.15	12.15	13.15	-- --	15.15	16.15	17.15
Haworth	Dep	11.20	12.20	13.20	14.20	15.20	16.20	17.20
Oxenhope	Arr	11.25	12.25	13.25	14.25	15.25	16.25	17.25

TABLE D OPERATES
HERITAGE DIESEL SERVICE
June 5th–9th, 12th–16th. October 23rd–27th.

TABLE E

		DSAT	DSAT	D	D	D	D	D
Oxenhope	Dep	09.00	09.55	11.15	12.25	13.35	14.45	15.55
Haworth	Dep	09.05	10.00	11.20	12.30	13.40	14.50	16.00
Oakworth	Dep	09.08	10.03	11.23	12.33	13.43	14.53	16.03
Damems	R	09.18	10.08	11.30	12.40	13.50	15.00	16.10
Ingrow	Dep	09.20	10.10	11.33	12.43	13.53	15.03	16.13
Keighley	Arr	09.25	10.15	11.40	12.50	14.00	15.10	16.20
Keighley	Dep	09.30	10.48	11.58	13.08	14.18	15.28	17.03
Ingrow	Dep	09.35	10.53	12.03	13.13	14.23	15.33	17.08
Damems	R	09.37	10.55	12.05	13.15	14.25	15.35	17.10
Oakworth	Dep	09.40	11.00	12.10	13.20	14.30	15.40	17.12
Haworth	Dep	09.45	11.05	12.13	13.23	14.33	15.43	17.15
Oxenhope	Arr	09.50	11.10	12.17	13.27	14.37	15.47	17.20

TABLE E OPERATES
PRE-CHRISTMAS WEEKENDS
December 2nd/3rd, 9th/10th,16th/17th, 23rd/24th.

NOTES
D: Diesel Heritage Service
R: Request Stop

1995 SPECIAL EVENTS

Enthusiasts' Weekend	April 1st/2nd
Horses on a Country Branch Line	May 20th/21st
Friends of *Thomas the Tank Engine*	June 3rd/4th, June 10th/11th
Steam & Diesel Weekend	July 1st/2nd
Family Weekend	August 12th/13th
Enthusiasts' Weekend	Sept 30th/Oct 1st

30 Steam Locos, 8 Diesels

FARES

Adults	£ 4.80
Child/OAP	£ 2.40
Family	£12.00
Day Rover	£ 6.00
Family Day Rover	£14.00

Rovers not normally available on Special Event dates.

Special Day Rovers and some standard fares available.

Length of operating line 4¾ miles

1995 LOCO FLEET
78022, 47279, 75078, 1054, 48431, 5775, 5305, 45596.

Lineside photographic passes – £5.00 Members Only.

WINE & DINE
'White Rose Pullman' – various evenings, pre-booked.

BED & BREAKFAST
Bridge House 01535 642372,   Ferncliffe 01535 643405,
Woodlands Grange 01535 646814.

Whilst not the longest line in steam circles, they pack an enormous amount into their five miles – award winning stations which combine to form Britain's third largest gas lighting system, and superbly turned out locos to get you between them all. The filming of *The Railway Children* brought the Worth Valley to the silver screen and they've never looked back!

FACILITIES
Souvenir Shop, Footplate Courses, Bar, On-Train Buffet, Light Refreshments, Museums, Car Parks, Picnic Site.

3F Class 'Jinty' No. 47279 on the Keighley & Worth Valley Railway

Eric Sawford

SR S15 No. 30506 – one of many ex-SR locomotives on the Mid-Hants Railway – stands at Ropley. Note the excellent topiary!

Eric Sawford

Kent & East Sussex Railway

Kent

STANDARD GAUGE

HEADQUARTERS
> Tenterden Town Station, Tenterden, Kent, TN30 6HE

PRINCIPAL STAIONS
> Tenterden Town, Northiam

HOW TO GET THERE
> Road: Tenterden & Northiam stations are signposted from A2070/A259 Ashford/Hastings Road
> Bus: Maidstone & District Services. Tel 01634 832666
> Rail: Headcorn, 8 miles, Ashford (Kent), 10 miles then M & D service 400 to Tenterden from Ashford

☎ Information   01580 762943   Enquiries   01580 765155
             01580 766428   Fax   01580 765654

TIMES

All Tables
Most trains call also at Rolvenden and Wittersham Road Stations.

TABLE A

Tenterden	Dep	11.30	13.30	15.30
Northiam	Arr	12.00	14.00	16.00
Northiam	Dep	12.15	14.15	16.15
Tenterden	Arr	12.55	14.55	16.55

Note: D
This service runs as Hastings line diesel train in March, November & on Saturdays in April, May September and October.

TABLE B

			D		D		D
Tenterden	Dep	11.00	12.00	13.00	14.00	15.00	16.00
Northiam	Arr	11.30	12.30	13.30	14.30	15.30	16.30
Northiam	Dep	11.45	12.45	13.45	14.45	15.45	16.45
Tenterden	Arr	12.25	13.25	14.25	15.25	16.25	17.20

TABLE C

Tenterden	Dep	10.30	11.00	12.00	13.00	13.40	14.10	15.00	15.30	16.30
Northiam	Arr	11.00	11.35	12.35	13.30	14.10	14.45	15.30	16.00	17.00
Northiam	Dep	11.15	11.50	12.45	13.45	14.20	15.05	15.40	16.15	17.15
Tenterden	Arr	11.50	12.25	13.20	14.30	14.55	15.50	16.15	16.50	17.50

TABLE A OPERATES   Off-Peak Weekdays
April 18th–21st. June 6th–8th, 13th–15th, 20th–22nd, 27th–29th.
July 3rd–7th, 10th–14th, 17th–21st. September 5th–7th, 12th–14th, 19th–21st, 26th–28th.

TABLE B OPERATES   Standard Service
March 12th, 19th, 26th. April 1st/2nd, 8th/9th, 22nd/23rd, 29th/30th.
May 13th/14th, 20th/21st, 30th/31st. June 1st/2nd, 10th/11th, 17th/18th, 24th/25th.
July 8th, 15th, 22nd, 24th–29th, 31st.
August 1st–4th, 7th–12th, 14th–19th, 21st–25th, 29th–31st.
September 1st–3rd, 16th/17th, 23rd/24th, 30th. October 1st, 7th/8th, 21st/22nd, 28th/29th.
November 12th, 19th.

TABLE C OPERATES   Peak Sundays
July 9th, 16th, 23rd, 30th. August 13th, 20th.
On Special Event Days (listed on next page) a frequent service operates 10.00–16.30.

1995 SPECIAL EVENTS

Easter Family Fun	April 14th–17th
VE-Day 50th	May 7th/8th
21st Anniversary	
Steam Spectacular	June 3rd/4th
Friends of *Thomas*	
the Tank Engine	July 1st/2nd
Behind the Scenes	
Weekend	August 5th/6th
Festival of Steam & Song	September 9th/10th
Diesel Gala	October 14th/15th
Santa Trains	December Weekends
	& 21st/22nd.

FARES

Adults £6.00, Child £2.00
OAP £5.00, Family £15.00
Pay once - travel all day.
excluding Bank Holidays and
Special Events.

Length of operating line 7 miles

Lineside photographic passes
£12.00 annum (non members)

15 Steam Locos, 10 Diesels

WINE & DINE

'Wealden Pullman' – Saturday evenings. 'Rother Valley Limited' – Sunday lunch.
Pre-book only.

The Kent & East Sussex was one of England's classic rural railways, connecting
Robertsbridge and Headcorn on the main railway system. The centre section of this route is
now steam operated with sights on extending to Bodiam. Although never part of the Southern
Railway, the rolling stock and atmosphere has a Southern feel to it. The 'Vintage Train' is a
superb example of rolling stock restoration.

FACILITIES

Souvenir Shop, Footplate Courses, Light Refreshments, On-Train Buffet, Museum, Car Park,
Disabled Facilities, Picnic Site. Childrens' Tea Parties, Railway Experience courses inc.
Driving, Firing, Signalling and Guard duties.
Tenterden site open daily except December 25th/26th.

AUCTIONS OF RAILWAYANA, POSTERS, MODELS & ADVERTISING.

We hold regular Auctions selling all items from our railway heritage. We are especially
renowned for our nameplate sales (having achieved a world record price of £20,400 for a
nameplate) but we sell everything from posters to clocks, signalling devices to station
signs, lamps to tableware, photographs to cast - iron signs, O gauge to live steam
models, enamel advertising signs to vending machines, platform seats to lamp - posts,
postcards, tickets, books, etc, etc. Whole libraries and collections to single items.
The Auctions are held in Sheffield and consist of 500 lots. We regularly attract 500 - 600
attendance and have a subscription - list for our catalogues of 1000 +, including all the
major Museums. We have many overseas customers.
Unlike most other Auctions we do not charge a Buyers' Premium.
Our commission - rate to vendors is only 10% (plus VAT) on items up to £1000,
5% plus VAT thereafter. There are no other charges.

AUCTION DATES IN 1995
MAIN AUCTIONS: March 18th, June 17th, September 16th, December 9th.
POSTAL BOOK /EPHEMERA AUCTIONS: Mar 18, June 17, Sept 16, Dec 9.
POSTAL - TICKET AUCTIONS: February, April, June, August, November.
Illustrated Catalogues £3.50 (£10 For 3, £18 for 6 on Subscription)
SHEFFIELD RAILWAYANA AUCTIONS
43, Little Norton Lane, Sheffield, S8 8GA
TEL/FAX 01142 745085

Southern Railway W24 *Calbourne* takes on water at the Isle of Wight Steam Railway's
western terminus of Wootton

Paul Appleton

MANAGEMENT & MARKETING LTD

Consultants to Outdoor Event Organisers, we specialise in arranging
Trade Stand and Catering Concessions, Arena Entertainment and
attractions for

★ **STEAM & VINTAGE RALLIES (including Bluebell Railway
Steam & Vintage Rally)** ★ **FESTIVALS** ★ **GALAS** ★ **ETC** ★

Anywhere UK. Let us quote for your Special Event.

119 Thorpe Road, Peterborough, PE3 6JH. Tel: 01773 894440

Kirklees Light Railway

West Yorkshire

'Yorkshire's Great Little Train'

NARROW GAUGE

HEADQUARTERS
> The Railway Station, Park Mill Way, Clayton West, Huddersfield, HD8 9PE

PRINCIPAL STATIONS
> Clayton West, Skelmanthorpe

HOW TO GET THERE
> Road: M1 Jct 38 or 39, thence A636 towards Denby Dale
> Rail: Wakefield, 9 miles, then bus No. 484, 235

☎ Information 01484 865727

TIMES

Clayton West   Dep   11.00   12.00   13.00   14.00   15.00   16.00   17.00

(on demand)

45 minute trip.

SERVICE OPERATES

> SUMMER –   Every day from Easter to September.
> WINTER –   Every weekend, as above on Sundays, but 13.00 start Saturdays.

1995 SPECIAL EVENTS

Miniature Traction Engine Rally	April 29th/30th
Wild West Weekend (fancy dress)	June 3rd/4th
Teddy Bears' Picnic	June 24th/25th
Friends of *Thomas the Tank Engine*	July 15th/16th
	September 2nd/3rd
Halloween Ghost Trains	October 28th/29th
Santa Specials	December weekends.

FARES

Adults	£3.00	3 Steam Locos inc. 2–6–2T *Fox*
Child	£2.25	2–6–2 No.2 – Sandy River American Outline
Under 2	Free	1 Diesel. 0–6–4ST *Badger*

Length of operating line 2 miles

The 15" gauge rolling stock and locomotives have been built in the railway's own workshops and run on the trackbed of the former Lancashire and Yorkshire Railway.

FACILITIES

Souvenir Shop, Light Refreshments, Disabled Facilities, Picnic Site, Car Park, Model Railway, half-scale Fairground.

Lakeside & Haverthwaite Railway Cumbria

STANDARD GAUGE

HEADQUARTERS
   Haverthwaite Station, Nr Ulverston, Cumbria, LA12 8AL
PRINCIPAL STATIONS
   Haverthwaite, Lakeside
HOW TO GET THERE
   Road: On A590 Ulverstone Road
   Bus: Cumberland Motor Services from Windermere
   Rail: Ulverstone, 7 miles
   Water: via Windermere Iron Steamboat Co.

☎ Information 01539 531594

TIMES
TABLE A

							B	A
Haverthwaite	Dep	10.40	11.45	13.00	14.05	15.10	16.15	17.20
Newby Bridge	Dep	10.52	11.57	13.12	14.17	15.22	16.27	17.32
Lakeside	Arr	10.58	12.03	13.18	14.23	15.28	16.33	17.38
Windermere Steamer	Arr	11.05	12.20	13.25	14.30	15.35	16.40	17.40
Windermere Steamer	Dep	11.20	12.30	13.35	14.40	15.45	16.55	D- --
							B	A
Lakeside	Dep	11.15	12.30	13.35	14.40	15.45	16.50	17.48
Newby Bridge	Dep	11.21	12.36	13.41	14.46	15.51	16.56	17.54
Haverthwaite	Arr	11.33	12.48	13.53	14.58	16.03	17.08	18.06

SERVICE OPERATES

Daily April 8th–23rd, 29th–November 5th.
A: Operates May 28th–June 4th. July 23rd–September 3rd and may be diesel hauled.
B: Operates until October 28th.
D: Boat sails April 14th–23rd & May 6th–September 27th.
Combine rail trip with cruise on the lake to Ambleside and return.

FARES (Railway)
Adults £3.10 Child £1.55

Length of operating line 3½ miles

10 Steam Locos, 9 Diesels

An ex-Furness Railway branch line that used to run from Ulverston. A heavily graded line brings you to the Lakeside terminus with connections to the Windermere Iron Steamboat Co's boats which ply the length of Windermere – and back in time for tea at one of the best buffets in railway preservation.

1995 LOCOS
42085/Fairburn 2–6–4T
Austerity 0–6–0ST *Cumbria*
Austerity 0–6–0ST *Repulse*
Bagnall 0–6–0ST *Princess*

FACILITIES
Souvenir Shop, Light Refreshments, Full Meals, Licensed Bar, Disabled Toilet, Picnic Site, Car Park, Childrens' Parties.

LAUNCESTON STEAM RAILWAY

Cornwall

NARROW GAUGE

HEADQUARTERS
The Station, St. Thomas Road, Launceston, Cornwall, PL15 8DA
PRINCIPAL STATIONS
Launceston, New Mills
HOW TO GET THERE
Road: A388, Car Park on Launcestons' Newport Industrial Estate
Bus: Western National 01752 222666
Rail: Gunnislake, 12 miles, Liskeard, 20 miles

☎ Information 01566 775665

TIMES

Launceston	Dep	11.00	11.50	12.40	14.00	14.40	15.35	16.30
New Mills	Dep	11.20	12.10	13.00	14.20	15.00	15.55	17.00

SERVICE OPERATES

Good Friday to Easter Monday inclusive. Thence every Tuesday and Sunday until Whitsun.
Daily from Whitsun until September 30th, except Sats.
October Tuesdays & Sundays.

Having completed the extension to New Mills in 1994, you can now travel further behind a Hunslet Quarry engine on the trackbed of the former LSWR line from Halwill to Padstow.

1995 SPECIAL EVENTS

Santa Specials   Weekends in December
Mince Pie Specials   December 26th until
New Year

FARES

Adult Return	£3.50
Children	£2.80
OAP	£3.00
Family	£11.00

(Two Adults and up to 4 Children)

1995 LOCO FLEET
Hunslet 317 – 1883 *Lilian*
Hunslet 409 – 1886 *Velinheli*
Hunslet 679 – 1898 *Covertcoat*

Length of operating line
2½ miles

FACILITIES
Souvenir Shop, Light Refreshments, Full Meals, Museum, Car Park, Picnic Site, Disabled Coach.

Lavender Line

Sussex

HEADQUARTERS
Isfield Station, Isfield, Near Uckfield, East Sussex, TN22 5XB
PRINCIPAL STATION
Isfield
HOW TO GET THERE
Road: Off A26 Lewes–Uckfield road
Bus: 729 Brighton to Tunbridge Wells Service times. Tel 01273 206666
Rail: Lewes, 5 miles. Uckfield, 4 miles

☎ Information 01825 750515 Catering & Function Enquiries 01825 750256

TIMES
Trains leave Isfield frequently depending on demand, usally every 20–30 mins from 11.00 to 17.00.

SERVICE OPERATES
Sundays March to December. Bank Holiday Saturdays & Mondays.
Also April 14th & daily during August.
Santa Specials November 25th/26th. December 2nd/3rd, 9th/10th, 16th/17th.

Services usually steam operated but may be DMU on certain low-season dates or early/late services.

Length of operating line ¾ mile (extension to 1 mile subject to HMRI approval)

FARES
Adults £3.00, Child £2.00
Unlimited travel on day of purchase.
Higher fares may apply on certain Special Event Days.

4 Steam Locos, 3 Diesels & 2 DMUs
Dock Tank *Cunarder*, 0–4–0 Barclay
J49 *Blackie* (later in 1995)
Diesels include unique Bulleid Class 12 No. 15224.

The beautifully restored ex-LBSCR station and signal box at Isfield present a wondrous site, completely junk-free! The preservation group are now very much in control after purchasing everything from the former owner. The motive power is just starting to get interesting, and with further extensions planned – it's all systems go. Incidentally, you may assume that 'Lavender' takes its name from plants along the line, as elsewhere, but it is actually the surname of the station's original coal merchant.

FACILITIES
Souvenir Shop, Light Refreshments, Full Meals, Museum, Car Park, Footplate Courses.
Museum housed in LNWR coach used by Earl Haig as mobile HQ in 1st World War.

Leadhills & Wanlockhead Rly   Lanarkshire

HEADQUARTERS
> The Station, Leadhills, Lanarkshire, ML12

PRINCIPAL STATION
> Leadhills

HOW TO GET THERE
> Road: 6 miles west on B747 off Jct 14 of M74
> Rail: Kirkconnel, 9 miles

☎   Enquiries   01461 202422
     Secretary   0141 339 9813

TIMES
> 11.00 to 17.00 continuous operation – as required.

SERVICE OPERATES
> Weekends from May to September incl. and April 15th/16th.

FARES
Adults £1.00, Child 50p, Family £2.50   Length of operating line ⅓ mile

It is the operating societies' objective to extend the line to Wanlockhead during 1995 which will take the line's length to 1¼ miles. The line between the former lead mining villages is above the 1400' contour with a ruling gradient of 1 in 40 making it the highest narrow gauge (2'0") adhesion railway in Great Britain. Wanlockhead was the terminus of the ex-Caledonian Railway branch from Elvanfoot.

5 Diesel Locos, 1 Steam Loco (being refurbished)

1995 LOCOS
Hunslet 6347 *Clyde*, Ruston's *Luce* & *Little Clyde*, Simplex *Elvan*

BED & BREAKFAST
Hopetown Hotel, Leadhills   01659 74234

FACILITIES
Souvenir Shop, Picnic Site, Car Park.

Leighton Buzzard Railway

Beds

'England's Friendly Little Line'　　　　　　　　**NARROW GAUGE**

HEADQUARTERS
　　　　Page's Park Station, Billington Road, Leighton Buzzard, Beds, LU7 8TN
PRINCIPAL STATIONS
　　　　Page's Park, Stonehenge Works
HOW TO GET THERE
　　　　Road:　Signposted in town. A505 Bypass to Station off A4146
　　　　Bus:　Luton & District to Town Centre, also Leisure Link
　　　　　　　Sunday Service. Tel: 01234 228337
　　　　Rail:　Leighton Buzzard, 2 miles

　Information 01525 373888

TIMES

		X			X			X		Y
Page's Park	Dep	11.00	11.40	12.30	13.10	13.50	14.30	15.10	15.50	16.30
Stonehenge	Arr	11.25	12.05	12.55	13.35	14.15	14.55	15.35	16.15	16.55
Stonehenge	Dep	11.35	12.25	13.05	13.45	14.25	15.05	15.45	16.25	17.05
Page's Park	Arr	12.00	12.40	13.30	14.10	14.50	15.30	16.10	16.50	17.30

SERVICE OPERATES
Sundays & Bank Holiday Mondays April 2nd to October 15th,
Wednesdays June 7th to August 30th. Thurdays August 3rd to 31st
Friday April 14th.
Saturdays April 15th, June 3rd, August 5th–26th, September 9th.

NOTES
　X. Runs April 16th/17th, 30th. May 7th/8th, 28th/29th. June 3rd/4th.
　　July 2nd, 9th, 16th, 23rd, 30th. August 6th, 13th, 20th, 27th/28th. September 9th/10th.

　Y. Runs each operating Sunday, Bank Holiday Mondays, June 3rd, September 9th.

Length of operating line 2¾ miles

11 Steam Locos, 40 Diesels

1995 LOCOS
Barclay 0–6–0T *Doll*, O&K 0–6–0 OWT *E/F*. Others scheduled to operate at major steam
events include: *Chaloner* (de Winton), *Rishra* (Baguley), *Peter Pan* & *Pixie* (Wren),
Alice (Hunslett).

1995 SPECIAL EVENTS

Teddy Bears Outing	April 30th
50 Years On (VE-Day)	May 8th
Heritage Weekend	June 3rd/4th
Iron Horse Wild West Day	July 2nd
Model Mania	August 6th
Autumn Steam-Up	September 9th/10th
Conker Championships	September 24th
Christmas Trains	Sats/Suns Dec 2nd–24th
Mince Pie Specials	December 26th

FARES

Adults £4.00, OAP £3.00
Child (2–15) £1.00

INDUSTRY TRAIN DISPLAYS

April 9th, May 7th, June 4th, July 9th, August 13th, September 10th, October 1st includes Demonstration Sand train, Loco viewing and working quarry displays.

Opened in 1919 for sand traffic, the line's 2" gauge loco fleet have come from all over the world. Combine with Grand Union Canal cruise. Tel. 01525 373888

FACILITIES

Souvenir Shop, Light Refreshments, Disabled Facilities, Museum Display, Picnic Site, Car Park. Photographic passes not required.

Gwynedd

NARROW GAUGE

HEADQUARTERS

Padarn Country Park, Llanberis, Gwynedd, LL55 4TY

PRINCIPAL STATIONS

Gilfach Ddu (Padarn Park), Cei Llydan, Penllyn

HOW TO GET THERE

Road: Just off A4086 Caernarfon/Capel Curig road (A5)
Bus: Gwynedd Services from Bangor via Caernarfon
Rail: Bangor, 9 miles

 Information 01286 870549

TIMES 11.00–15.00 (16.00/16.30 in high season) departures from Padarn Park. Daily March–October.

Length of operating line 2 miles

3 Steam Locos *Dolbadarn Elidiir, Thomas Bach*

Another line to view Snowdonia, built on the original quarry railway trackbed, skirting the lake shoreline and depositing you at the Welsh Slate Museum with its preserved machinery and giant waterwheel.

FARES

Adult Return	£3.80
Child	£2.00
Family	£9.60

(2 Adults & 2 Children)

FACILITIES

Souvenir Shop, Light Refreshments, Museum, Car Park, Disabled Toilet, Picnic Site. Located within Padarn Country Park. Welsh Slate Museum close by.

Llangollen Railway   Clwyd

Clwyd's Scenic Steam Railway   **STANDARD GAUGE**

HEADQUARTERS
> Llangollen Station, Abbey Road, Llangollen, Clwyd, LL20 8SN

PRINCIPAL STATIONS
> Langollen, Glyndyfrdwy

HOW TO GET THERE
> Road: On A542 off A5 between Chirk and Corwen
> Bus: From Ruabon to Llangollen
> Rail: Ruabon, 5 miles

 Information 01978 860951 Enquiries 01978 860979

TIMES

Llangollen	Dep	10.00	11.00	12.40	14.20	16.00
Glyndyfrdwy	Dep	10.28	11.42	13.22	15.02	16.42

The above table applies to the main daily running season. Extra trains run Sundays/Bank Holidays. Last train is 15.00 at beginning and end of season.

SERVICE OPERATES
> Every weekend throughout the year except December 25th.
> Daily from Easter to end of October.
> 1995 Timetable not finalised at time of going to press.

FARES

Adults	£5.00
Child	£2.50

6 Steam Locos
Visiting engines expected

WINE & DINE
'Berwyn Belle' departs Saturday evenings & Sunday lunch.
Telephone for details of running dates to Bryn Dderwen Hotel 01978 860583.
Length of operating line 5½ miles

Llangollen Railway boasts some very attractive black and white timbered station buildings and well-kept gardens to match. The line nestles in nicely between the A5 trunk road and the River Dee, famous for its canoe sports and spot of salmon. The line used to provide a link between Ruabon and the Cambrian Coast at Barmouth, bringing the tourists from the industrial areas of the North West, and still bringing the tourists in as an attraction in its own right!

Llangollen Canal trips available as combined rail/boat trip for party bookings.
Tel. 01691 75322.

FACILITIES
Souvenir Shop, Light Refreshments, Full Meals, On-Train Buffet, Model Railway, Picnic Site (Glyndyfrdwy), Footplate Courses.
Car Park – Llangollen & Berwyn. Disabled – 2 weeks notice.

RAILWAY
MANGAPPS FARM
MUSEUM

HEADQUARTERS
Mangapps Farm, Burnham-on-Crouch, Essex, CM0 8QQ

HOW TO GET THERE
Road: B1010/B1021 via Burnham-on-Crouch
Bus: Eastern National passes entrance
Rail: Burnham-on-Crouch, 1 mile

☎   Information & Fax 01621 784898

TIMES
Steam Days 11.30 to 17.00.   Diesel Days 13.00 to 18.00.
Trains run every 30 minutes or every 15 minutes according to demand.

SERVICE OPERATES
Every Saturday & Sunday, Bank Holidays except December 25th/26th.
All school holidays.

Steam trains operate first Sunday in month, Bank Holiday and Sundays preceeding
Bank Holidays. Every Sunday in August and certain Special Events.
Half hour intervals, or more frequently if required.

Diesel trains operate on all other days that the railway is open.

Length of operating line ½ mile – extending during 1995

1995 SPECIAL EVENTS
Friends of *Thomas*
the Tank Engine   April 1st/2nd
                           June 17th/18th
                           Nov 4th/5th

Transport Gala/Model
Railway Exhibition   July 2nd
Freight Day (Steam & Diesel)   Sept 3rd/Oct 1st
Santa Specials   Dec 3rd, 9th/10th
                           16th/17th, 23rd/24th
Mince Pie Specials   Dec 31st/Jan 1st.

FARES
Steam Days Adult £4.00,
Child £2.50, OAP £3.50
(less for Diesel days,
premium on Special Events)

3 Steam Locos, 6 Diesels,
1 DMU

BED & BREAKFAST
White Horse   01621 782106
Cromwell House 01621 783654

Created from a greenfield site, it boasts a wondrous exhibition hall of small relics.
Bagnall's 0–6–0 ST *Demelza* and 0–6–0 PT *Brookfield* lead the steam line-up for 1995.

FACILITIES
Souvenir Shop, Light Refreshments, Museum, Picnic Site, Car Park.

Middleton Railway

West Yorkshire

HEADQUARTERS
> The Station, Moor Road, Leeds, LS10 2JQ

PRINCIPAL STATIONS
> Moor Road, Middleton Park

HOW TO GET THERE
> Road: M1 Exit 45 or A653
> Rail: Leeds, 2 miles

☎ Information 01532 710320

TIMES (from Moor Road)
> Saturdays   13.10 and every 40 minutes until 16.30
> Sundays   11.50 and every 40 minutes until 16.30
> Special timetables on Special Event Days – Trains from 10.30
> 25 minute round trip.

SERVICE OPERATES
> Every weekend from April 1st to January 1st.

1995 SPECIAL EVENTS

May Day Family Weekend	May 7th/8th
Friends of *Thomas*	May 20th/21st
the Tank Engine	October 21st/22nd
Postman Pat Day	June 23rd
Teddy Bears' Picnic	August 20th
Gala Weekend	September 23rd/24th
Santa Trains	November 26th
	December 2nd/3rd, 9th/10th, 16th/17th.
Thomas' New Year Party	Dec 29th–Jan 1st

New Museum building opening end of 1995
New running/works shed now open for viewing

FARES (subject to revision)
> Adults £1.60
> Child 80p
> Family £4.50

All Day
> Adults £3.00
> Child £1.50

Length of operating line 1½ miles

12 Steam Locos, 8 Diesels

1995 LOCOS
1310: *Mirvale*: 385, 1601, 68153, 91, 138C

First railway to be opened by Act of Parliament 1758 *'The World's Oldest Railway'*.

MSC 67, Hudswell 0–6–0T moves from Keighley to Middleton Railway in 1995.

FACILITIES

Souvenir Shop, Light Refreshments, Car Park. Special Fares apply for Special Events.

Mid·hants WATERCRESS LINE

Hampshire

STANDARD GAUGE

HEADQUARTERS
    Alresford Station, Alresford, Hants, SO24 9JG
PRINCIPAL STATIONS
    Alresford, Ropley, Medstead, Alton
HOW TO GET THERE
    Road: Alresford and Alton Stations are just off A31 Guildford–Winchester road
    Bus: Stagecoach to Alton/Alresford. Hampshire Bus. Tel 01962 852352
    Rail: Alton (adjacent platform)

☎ Information 01962 734866 Enquiries 01962 733810 Fax 01962 735448

TIMES

TABLE A

Alresford	Dep	10.40	12.25	14.25	16.10
Ropley	Dep	10.55	12.39	14.39	16.26
Medstead	Dep	11.05	12.49	14.49	16.36
Alton	Arr	11.18	13.02	15.02	16.50
Alton	Dep	11.30	13.25	15.25	17.00
Medstead	Dep	11.44	13.39	15.39	17.14
Ropley	Dep	11.55	13.55	15.49	17.23
Alresford	Arr	12.03	14.03	15.57	17.30

TABLE A OPERATES
March 12th, 19th. May 30th/31st.
June 1st/2nd, 6th–8th, 13th–15th,
20th–22nd, 27th–29th.
July – Weekdays. August 1st–4th,
7th–11th, 21st–25th, 29th–31st.
September 1st. October 24th–26th.

TABLE B

Alton	Dep	10.45	12.30	14.25	15.55
Medstead	Dep	10.59	12.44	14.39	16.09
Ropley	Dep	11.09	12.55	14.49	16.18
Alresford	Arr	11.17	13.03	14.58	16.26
Alresford	Dep	11.30	13.25	15.10	16.45
Ropley	Dep	11.43	13.39	15.23	16.58
Medstead	Dep	11.53	13.50	15.33	17.08
Alton	Arr	12.06	14.03	15.46	17.21

TABLE B OPERATES
March 11th, 18th, 25th.
April 1st, 8th, 29th. May 13th, 20th.
June 3rd, 10th, 17th, 24th.
September 9th, 23rd, 30th.
October 7th, 14th, 21st.

TABLE C

Alresford	Dep	-- --	10.12	11.12	12.12	13.12	14.12	15.12	16.12	17.12
Ropley	Dep	-- --	10.27	11.27	12.27	13.27	14.27	15.27	16.27	17.27
Meadstead	Dep	-- --	10.40	11.40	12.40	13.40	14.40	15.40	16.40	17.37
Alton	Arr	-- --	10.53	11.53	12.53	13.53	15.53	15.53	16.53	17.50
Alton	Dep	10.25	11.25	12.25	13.25	14.25	15.25	16.25	17.03	-- --
Meadstead	Dep	10.39	11.39	12.39	13.39	14.39	15.39	16.39	17.16	-- --
Ropley	Dep	10.50	11.50	12.50	13.50	14.50	15.50	16.50	17.26	-- --
Alresford	Arr	10.58	11.58	12.58	13.58	14.58	15.58	16.58	17.34	-- --

TABLE C OPERATES April 2nd, 9th, 30th. May 6th–8th, 14th, 21st.
June 4th, 11th, 18th, 25th. July 8th,/9th, 15th/16th, 22nd/23rd, 29th/30th.
August 5th/6th, 26th–28th. September 10th, 24th. October 1st, 8th, 15th, 22nd.

1995 SPECIAL EVENTS

Diesel Weekend	March 4th/5th
Mother's Day Teas	March 26th
Friends of *Thomas*	
the Tank Engine	April 14th-23rd
	August 12th-20th
VE-Day	May 6th-8th
Return to Alton	May 27th-29th
Father's Day	June 18th
Bus Rally	July 1st/2nd
War on the Line	September 2nd/3rd
Diesel Weekend	September 16th/17th
Teddy Bears' Day	October 1st
Enthusiasts' Weekend	October 28th/29th
Santa Trains	December Weekends

FARES

Adults	£7.50
Child	£4.50
OAP	£5.50
Family	£22.00

(2 Adults & 4 Children)

Disabled passengers are welcome. It is recommended that passengers telephone in advance of their visit to ensure reserved accommodation as space is limited.
Toilet facilities –
Ropley Station only.

BED & BREAKFAST

The Old Manse	01962 734396
Mrs Elliott	01962 732605

WINE & DINE

'The Countryman' Sunday lunch & afternoon tea
'Watercress Belle' Saturday evenings

Length of operating line 10 miles

8 Steam Locos, 4 Diesels

1995 LOCOS

76017 Std 4, 73080 Std 5, 30506 S15, 34105, WD701. *Thomas the Tank*, *James the Red Engine*.

The original Mid-Hants route between Alton and Winchester was known as 'over the Alps' by enginemen due to the line being steeply graded. Like Bluebell and Swanage, this line is pure Southern Railway with its locos and stations of ex-SR vintage. Ropley Station is decorated LSWR style and boasts one of the finest displays of topiary to be found anywhere, looked after and pruned since BR days.

The Mid-Hants also cram more Santa Special passengers than most other lines, and have surely benefitted from their BR link.

FACILITIES

Souvenir Shop, Light Refreshments, Picnic Area (Ropley), Children's Birthday Parties, Car Park – Alton & Alresford Pay & Display (free Sundays / Bank Holidays). No Parking Facilities at Ropley & Medstead, Museum, Schools Facility. Visits to Bass Brewery, Alton – pre-booked tickets.

Derbyshire

STANDARD GAUGE
NARROW GAUGE
MINIATURE GAUGE

HEADQUARTERS
Butterley Station, Ripley, Derbyshire, DE5 3QZ
PRINCIPAL STATIONS
Butterley – Swanwick Junction, Riddings – Hammersmith
HOW TO GET THERE
Road: Junction 28 on M1, signposted from A38 on B6179,
         1 mile north of Ripley
Bus: Trent Buses 148, 242, 243, 245. Tel 01332 292200
Rail: Alfreton & Mansfield Parkway, 5 miles. Derby, 10 miles

☎ Information 01773 570140, 01773 747674 Fax 01773 570721

TIMES Return Trip 50 minutes.

TABLE A (Mid Season)
Butterley	Dep	11.15	12.30	14.00	15.00	16.15

TABLE B (High Season)
Butterley	Dep	10.45	11.45	12.45	14.00	15.00	16.15

TABLE C (Two Train Service)
Butterley	Dep	10.45	11.20	11.55	12.30	13.05	14.00	14.35	15.10	15.45	16.20

TABLE A OPERATES
March 12th, 25th. April 1st, 12th, 13th, 19th–22nd, 26th. May 3rd, 10th, 17th, 24th.
June 7th, 19th/20th, 28th/29th. July 1st, 4th–6th, 11th–13th. August 30th/31st.
September 1st/2nd, 6th, 13th, 20th, 23rd, 27th. October 4th, 7th, 11th, 18th. November 4th.

TABLE B OPERATES
April 8th, 14th/15th, 18th, 29th. May 6th, 20th, 27th, 30th/31st.
June 1st–3rd, 10th, 21st/22nd. July 8th, 15th, 18th–20th, 24th–29th, 31st.
August 1st–4th, 14th–18th, 21st–25th, 29th. September 16th, 24th.
October 1st, 8th, 21st, 23rd–29th.

TABLE C OPERATES
March 4th/5th, 26th. April 2nd, 9th, 16th/17th, 23rd, 30th. May 7th/8th, 21st, 28th/29th.
June 4th, 11th. July 2nd, 9th, 16th, 30th. August 19th/20th. September 3rd, 17th, 30th.
October 22nd.

SPECIAL SERVICE OPERATES
March 11th, 18th/19th, 29th. April 5th.
May 9th, 11th/12th, 13th–16th, 18th, 22nd/23rd, 25th.
June 6th, 8th, 17th/18th, 24th/25th, 27th, 30th. July 7th, 14th, 21st–23rd.
August 5th–13th, 26th–28th. September 5th, 7th–10th, 12th, 14th, 21st.
October 14th/15th. November 5th, 12th, 19th, 25th/26th. December.

1995 SPECIAL EVENTS

Diesel Locomotive Gala	March 18th/19th
Mother's Day Sunday Lunch	March 26th
Spring on the Farm	April 1st/2nd
Easter Eggstravaganza	April 12th–23rd
Nostalgia Weekend	
Half Price for Senior Citizens	April 29th/30th
VE-Day Celebrations	May 6th–8th
Anniversary Steam Gala	May 13th/14th
Model Railway Exhibition	May 13th/14th
Thomas the Tank Engine	May 27th–June 4th
Father's Day Sunday Lunch	June 18th
Schools Week	June 12th–22nd
Edwardian Gala	June 24th/25th
Road Transport Display & Rally	July 2nd
Farm & Country Fair	July 15th/16th
Summer Diesel Spectacular	July 21st–23rd
Free for Registered Disabled	July 29th/30th
Thomas the Tank Engine	August 5th–13th
Narrow Gauge Railway Event & Garden Railway Festival	August 19th/20th
Victorian Gala	August 26th–28th
Miniature Railway Event	August 27th/28th
Grand Steam Gala	September 9th/10th
Stationary Power Display	October 7th/8th
Autumn Diesel Spectacular	October 14th/15th
Oswald the Talking Engine's Birthday Party	October 21st–29th
Fireworks Night	November 4th

FARES

Adult £5.95, OAP £4.95. Sundays & Bank Holiday Adult £6.95, OAP £5.95, up to 2 children free with each adult or OAP. Includes unlimited travel on Narrow and Standard gauge lines and admission to museum, country park and animal farm.

WINE & DINE

'Midlander'. Sunday lunch, afternoon tea, Childrens' Parties & Charter Service

21 Standard Gauge Locos, 21 diesels
4 Narrow Gauge Locos, 12 diesels

Length of operating line:
Standard Gauge 3½ miles
Narrow Gauge ¼ mile
Minimum Gauge ⅙ mile

BED & BREAKFAST

Spinney Lodge   01773 740168
The Kestrel   01773 743970

This is the railway with more special events than some railways have operating days! Seriously though, with three gauges on site, garden railway, model railway, country park and excellent museum, do allow yourself time to get the most from your visit. Home of LMS *Princess Margaret Rose* and many a mainline diesel – Butterley Station is pure Midland Railway.

FACILITIES

Souvenir Shop, Light Refreshments, Full Meals, On-Train Buffet, Museum, Disabled Toilet & access, Picnic Site, Car Park, Footplate Courses.

Mull and West Highland Railway   Isle of Mull

MULL RAIL   MINIMUM GAUGE

HEADQUARTERS
Old Pier Station, Craignure, Isle of Mull, Argyll, PA65 6AY
PRINCIPAL STATIONS
Craignure Old Pier, Torosay
HOW TO GET THERE
Road: ½ mile from ferry terminal at Craignure
Rail: Oban, 11 miles (on ferry)
40 minute sailing (Caledonian MacBrayne)

☎   Enquiries 01680 812 494   Admin 01680 300 389   Fax   01680 300 595

SERVICE OPERATES
All trains run in connection with ferry sailing times, Oban–Craignure.

TABLE A – High Season Mon–Fri May 29th–Sept 1st
Craignure Dep 11.10 11.20 11.50 12.30 13.10 13.30 14.20 15.10 15.25 15.35 16.35
17.00 (not Fri)

TABLE B – Early Late Season DAILY incl. Sundays April 13th–May 28th incl.
September 2nd–October 14th incl.
X
Craignure Dep 11.15 13.15 14.30 15.10 16.45
X commences May 15th, ceases September 17th.

TABLE C – High Season – Saturday & Sunday Only. June 3rd–August 27th.
Craignure Dep 11.15 13.15 14.30 15.15 16.45

FARES

Length of operating line 1¼ miles

Adults £2.50, Child £1.70
Family (2 adults & children) £6.50

3 Steam Locos, 2 Diesels

Steam Loco *Victoria* is believed to be the
BED & BREAKFAST   largest tank loco to be built in 10¼" gauge.
01680 812402 / 812442 /812423 / 812491

The only island railway in the UK that links with a major ferry operator (joint ticketing)
and the first island passenger railway in Scotland.
Travel from the Old Pier at Craignure to the Gardens of Torosay Castle.

FACILITIES

Souvenir Shop, Car Park, Disabled Coach.

Nene Valley Railway

Cambs

'Britain's International Steam Railway'   STANDARD GAUGE

1995 - PETERBOROUGH RAIL 150

HEADQUARTERS
Wansford Station, Stibbington, Peterborough, Cambridgeshire, PE8 6LR

PRINCIPAL STATIONS
Wansford, Peterborough (Nene Valley)

HOW TO GET THERE

Road:	Beside A1 at Stibbington
Bus:	From Peterborough to Orton Mere & Ferry Meadows
Rail:	Peterborough, 10 minutes walk

☎ Information 01780 782921 (& Fax service) Enquiries 01780 782854

TIMES

TABLE A   Bank Holidays & Major Event Service

Wansford	Dep	10.30	11.30	12.30	13.30	14.30	15.30	16.30
Yarwell Jct	Arr	10.35	11.35	12.35	13.35	14.35	15.35	16.35
Wansford	Dep	10.45	11.45	12.45	13.45	14.45	15.45	16.45
Ferry Meadows	Dep	10.58	11.58	12.58	13.58	14.58	15.58	16.58
Orton Mere	Dep	11.04	12.04	13.04	14.04	15.04	16.04	17.04
Peterborough N.V	Arr	11.10	12.10	13.10	14.10	15.10	16.10	17.10
Peterborough N.V	Dep	11.20	12.20	13.20	14.20	15.20	16.20	17.20
Orton Mere	Dep	11.27	12.27	13.27	14.27	15.27	16.27	17.27
Ferry Meadows	Dep	11.32	12.32	13.32	14.32	15.32	16.32	17.32
Wansford	Arr	11.44	12.44	13.44	14.44	15.44	16.44	17.44

TABLE A OPERATES
April 16th/17th. May 6th–8th, 27th–29th. June 3rd/4th, 24th/25th.
August 5th/6th, 26th–28th, September 16th/17th.

TABLE B   Summer Service

Wansford	Dep	10.30	12.00	13.30	15.00	16.30
Yarwell Jct	Arr	10.35	12.05	13.35	15.05	16.35
Wansford	Dep	10.45	12.15	13.45	15.15	16.45
Ferry Meadows	Dep	10.58	12.28	13.58	15.28	16.58
Orton Mere	Dep	11.04	12.34	14.04	15.34	17.04
Peterborough N.V	Dep	11.10	12.40	14.10	15.40	17.10
Peterborough N.V	Dep	11.20	12.50	14.20	15.50	17.20
Orton Mere	Dep	11.27	12.57	14.27	15.57	17.27
Ferry Meadows	Dep	11.32	13.02	14.32	16.02	17.32
Wansford	Arr	11.44	13.14	14.44	16.14	17.44

TABLE B OPERATES
June 10th/11th, 17th/18th. July weekends. August 12th/13th, 19th/20th.

TABLE C — Normal Service

					SSO
Wansford	Dep	11.30	13.15	15.00	16.30
Yarwell Jct	Arr	11.35	13.20	15.05	16.35
Wansford	Dep	11.50	13.35	15.20	16.45
Ferry Meadows	Dep	12.03	13.48	15.33	16.58
Orton Mere	Dep	12.09	13.54	15.39	17.04
Peterborough N.V	Arr	12.15	14.00	15.45	17.10
Peterborough N.V	Dep	12.30	14.15	16.00	17.20
Orton Mere	Dep	12.37	14.23	16.07	17.27
Ferry Meadows	Dep	12.42	14.28	16.12	17.32
Wansford	Arr	12.55	14.40	16.25	17.44

NOTE: SSO Sats & Suns only. Does not operate in March.

TABLE C OPERATES
March 5th, 11th/12th, 19th, 26th. April 1st/2nd, 8th/9th, 14th/15th, 18th–20th, 22nd/23rd, 29th/30th. May 13th/14th, 20th/21st, 30th/31st. June 1st. July 25th–28th. August all Tuesday to Friday dates. September 1st–3rd, 9th/10th, 23rd/24th, 30th. October weekends.

TABLE D — Midweek Service

Wansford	Dep	11.00	12.45	14.30
Yarwell Jct	Arr	11.05	12.50	14.35
Wansford	Dep	11.16	13.03	14.48
Ferry Meadows	Dep	11.30	13.18	15.00
Orton Mere	Dep	11.39	13.24	15.07
Peterborough N.V	Arr	11.45	13.30	15.13
Peterborough N.V	Dep	11.55	13.40	15.25
Orton Mere	Dep	12.01	13.46	15.31
Ferry Meadows	Dep	12.06	13.52	15.37
Wansford	Arr	12.20	14.05	15.50

TABLE D OPERATES
May 3rd, 10th, 17th, 24th. June 7th/8th, 14th/15th, 21st, 23rd, 28th. July 18th, 25th.

1995 SPECIAL EVENTS

Thomas Branch Line Days	March 11th/12th
Postal Seminar	March 25th
Easter Egg Hunt	April 14th–17th
European Weekend	May 6th–8th
Peterborough 150 Gala	June 2nd–4th
Thomas's Birthday	June 23rd–25th
Vintage Weekend	July 8th/9th
Open Weekend	July 22nd/23rd
Thomas's Big Weekend	August 5th/6th
Enthusiasts' Gala	Sept 16th/17th

Santa Trains/
Mince Pie Specials – Dec Weds, Sats & Suns.

21 Steam Locos, 15 Diesels
Bahamas visiting 1995
Length of operating line 7½ miles

FARES (for revision June 1995)
Adults £6.00, Child £3.00,
OAP & Disabled £4.50,
Family (2+2) £15.00.
All tickets unlimited travel on day of issue.

GOODS TRAIN
Demonstration Goods Train services –
3rd Saturday of each month
May–October

FACILITIES
Souvenir Shop, Light Refreshments, Full Meals, Museum Coach,
Disabled Facilities, Car Park.

Peterborough Rail 150

June 1995 sees the anniversary of the first train service to Peterborough 150 years ago.

To commemorate the event, the Nene Valley Railway will be holding a series of events throughout the year and will host a
Gala Weekend - June 2nd-4th
in conjunction with Peterborough City Tourism.

☆Visiting *Locomotion No.1* and LMS No 5596 (BR 45596) *Bahamas*
☆Grand Opening (June 2nd) - Cavalcade of Historic Trains
Beer Festival - Exhibitions - Vintage Vehicle Displays
Fairground - Street Theatre - Children's Entertainments
For Accommodation/Information contact:
Peterborough City Tourism 01733 317336
Nene Valley Railway 01780 782854

Ex-Polish Railways TY2 Class 2–10–0 No. 7173. Regular motive power on the Nene Valley Railway, pictured at Wansford Station

Eric Sawford

Northants

HEADQUARTERS
Northampton & Lamport Railway, Pitsford & Brampton Station,
Pitsford Road, Chapel Brampton, Northampton, NN6 8BA

PRINCIPAL STATION
Pitsford & Brampton

HOW TO GET THERE
Road: Off A50 at Chapel Brampton
Rail: Northampton, 5 miles

☎ Weekends   01604 820327

TIMES

TABLE A - Sundays in April and October (off peak)

Pitsford Stn	Dep	11.30	12.20	14.10	15.00	15.50
Pitsford Sdgs		--	----	----	----	--
Bridge 11	Arr	11.38	12.28	14.18	15.08	15.58
Bridge 11	Dep	11.40	12.30	14.20	15.10	16.00
Pitsford Sdgs		--	----	----	----	--
Pitsford Stn		--	----	----	----	--
Bridge 13	Arr	11.50	12.40	14.30	15.20	16.10
Bridge 13	Dep	11.52	12.42	14.32	15.22	16.12
Pitsford Stn	Arr	11.54	12.44	14.34	15.24	16.14

TABLE B - Sundays May 7th - September 24th (& Bank Holidays)

Pitsford Stn	Dep	10.30	11.10	11.50	12.30	13.20	14.00	14.40	15.20	16.00	16.45
Pitsford Sdgs		--	----	----	----	----	----	----	----	----	--
Bridge 11	Arr	10.38	11.18	11.58	12.38	13.28	14.08	14.48	15.28	16.08	16.52
Bridge 11	Dep	10.40	11.20	12.00	12.40	13.30	14.10	14.50	15.30	16.10	16.54
Pitsford Sdgs		--	----	----	----	----	----	----	----	----	--
Pitsford Stn		--	----	----	----	----	----	----	----	----	--
Bridge 13	Arr	10.50	11.30	12.10	12.50	13.40	14.20	15.00	15.40	16.20	17.05
Bridge 13	Dep	11.02	11.32	12.12	13.02	13.52	14.22	15.02	15.52	16.32	17.07
Pitsford Stn	Arr	11.04	11.34	12.14	13.04	13.54	14.24	15.04	15.54	16.34	17.09

Trains operate on Sundays & Bank Holidays only. No service January–March or November.

FARES
Adults £2.00, Child £1.25, Family £5.00

1995 SPECIAL EVENTS

Grand Official Opening	April 9th
Vintage Transport Rally	June 3rd/4th
Wartime Weekend	June 17th/18th
Teddy Bears' Picnic	August 27th/28th
Steam Gala	September 2nd/3rd
Diesel Gala	October 1st
Santa Trains	December 2nd–24th

4 Steam Locos, 7 Diesels
2 car DMU

1995 LOCOS
0–4–0 Peckett 2104
0–4–0 Cockerill 2945
Class 27

Length of operating line ¾ mile

A warm welcome to their first full year of timetabled operations, the Northampton & Lamport Railway Society have ambitious plans to relay track between the two towns, and have made a great start. The final BR years of this section was certainly staggered. First closed in 1960, re-opened to through traffic in January 1969, closed again in May of that year, re-opened in 1972, passenger service withdrawn in 1973 and finally closed in 1981.
We assume the current railway society are not superstitious. Good Luck!

FACILITIES
Souvenir Shop, Light Refreshments, Bar (adjacent), Car Park, Picnic Site.
Lineside photographic passes.

North Downs Steam Railway   Kent

'The Happy Line'

HEADQUARTERS
Cotton Lane Station, Cotton Lane, Stone, Dartford, Kent
PRINCIPAL STATIONS
Cotton Lane, London Road
HOW TO GET THERE
Road: M25 Junction 1 A, then Cotton Lane
Bus: 480 from Dartford
Rail: Dartford, 2 miles (then bus), Stone Crossing, 1 mile

   01322 228260

TIMES
From 11.00 to 17.00 Sundays January to November & Bank Holidays.
From 14.00 to 17.00 Saturdays June to September.

1995 SPECIAL EVENTS
Teddy Bears Picnic/Thomas events held spring/summer.

FARES
Adult £2.00, Child £1.00 (Steam)
Adult £1.50, Child 75p (Diesel)

2 Steam Locos, 7 Diesels
Length of operating line ½ mile

Based on a greenfield site, a short hop from the Dartford Tunnel and good views of the new QE2 Bridge.
Travel in ex-LT Met coaches, 'T' Stock (1952)

FACILITIES
Souvenir Shop, Light Refreshments, Car Park.

North Norfolk Railway
Norfolk

'The Poppy Line'   STANDARD GAUGE

HEADQUARTERS
> The Station, Sheringham, Norfolk, NR26 8RA

PRINCIPAL STATIONS
> Sheringham, Weybourne, Holt.

HOW TO GET THERE
> Road: Signposted off A148 Kings Lynn–Cromer road
> Bus: Eastern Counties route 758/9. Sanders Coaches
> Rail: Sheringham, 200 yds

☎ Information 01263 825449 Enquiries 01263 822045 Fax 01263 823794

TRAIN SERVICES
March – Sundays only (Steam)
April – Sundays & Daily Easter Week (Steam), Saturdays only (Diesel)
May – Saturdays & Sundays Only (Steam), Wednesdays & Thursdays (Diesel)
June – Daily, except Mondays (Steam), Fridays (Diesel)
July, August, September – daily
October – Sundays (Steam), Saturdays (Diesel). Daily October 21st–29th

NNR regret lack of full timetable available, whilst awaiting times for BR connection at Sheringham.

1995 SPECIAL EVENTS

B12 Weekend	March 3rd–7th
B12 Day	April 14th
Thomas Easter Egg Specials	April 15th/16th
B12 Day	April 17th
Diesel Weekend	June 3rd/4th
B12 Weekend	June 24th/25th
Model Railways	July 23rd
Gala Weekend	September 1st–3rd
Thomas Weekend	October 21st–23rd
Santa Specials/Mince Pie	December/January

WINE & DINE
East Coast Pullman
Saturday dinner, Sunday lunch.

Length of operating line 5¼ miles

6 Steam Locos, 4 Diesels

1995 LOCOS
3809 Austerity, 3824,
2107 *Harlaxton*,
B12, plus Guest Locos TBA

Looking at the list of Special Events, it seems the NNR are rightly proud of the return to traffic of the only surviving inside-cylinder 4–6–0 in the country – the ex-LNER B12 61572, having been rebuilt abroad. Lovely coastal scenery on this line – Weybourne station is beautifully restored and much in demand as a filming location.

FACILITIES
Souvenir Shop, Light Refreshments, Full Meals, On-Train Buffet, Museum, Car park, Disabled Toilet.

STANDARD GAUGE

HEADQUARTERS
Pickering Station, Pickering, North Yorkshire, YO18 7AJ
PRINCIPAL STATIONS
Pickering, Grosmont
HOW TO GET THERE
Road: Pickering is on A169/A170 in Pickering Town Centre
Bus: Yorkshire Coastliner Service. Tel 01653 692556
           Scarborough & District. Tel 01723 375463
Rail: Grosmont (adjacent)

☎ Information 01751 473535 Enquiries 01751 472508 Fax 01751 476970

TIMES

TABLE A

Grosmont	Dep	09.50	11.50	12.50	14.50	16.50
Goathland	Arr	10.05	12.05	13.05	15.05	17.05
Goathland	Dep	10.10	12.10	13.10	15.10	17.10
Newtondale		10.25	12.20	13.25	15.25	17.25
Levisham	Arr	10.36	12.36	13.36	15.36	17.36
Levisham	Dep	10.40	12.40	13.40	15.40	17.40
Pickering	Arr	10.57	12.57	13.57	15.57	17.57
Pickering	Dep	10.20	11.20	13.20	15.20	16.20
Levisham	Arr	10.37	11.37	13.37	15.37	16.37
Levisham	Dep	10.40	11.40	13.40	15.40	16.40
Newtondale		10.51	11.51	13.51	15.51	16.51
Goathland	Arr	11.06	12.06	14.06	16.06	17.06
Goathland	Dep	11.10	12.10	14.10	16.10	17.10
Grosmont	Arr	11.20	12.20	14.20	16.20	17.20

TABLE A OPERATES
April 1st, 3rd–8th, 10th–15th, 18th–22nd, 24th–29th. May 1st–6th, 9th–13th, 15th–20th,
22nd–27th. June 2nd/3rd, 5th–10th, 12th–16th, 19th–24th, 26th–30th. July 3rd–8th, 10th–15th,
17th–21st, 28th/29th. August 4th/5th, 11th/12th, 18th/19th, 25th/26th. September 1st/2nd,
4th–9th, 11th–15th, 18thv23rd, 25thv30th. October 2nd–6th, 9th–14th, 16th–21st, 23rd–27th.

TABLE B

					M		
Grosmont	Dep	09.50	11.50	12.50	13.50	14.50	16.50
Goathland	Arr	10.05	12.05	13.05	14.05	15.05	17.05
Goathland	Dep	10.10	12.10	13.10	14.10	15.10	17.10
Newtondale		10.25	12.20	13.25	14.25	15.25	17.25
Levisham	Arr	10.36	12.36	13.36	14.36	15.36	17.36
Levisham	Dep	10.40	12.40	13.40	14.40	15.40	17.40
Pickering	Arr	10.57	12.57	13.57	14.57	15.57	17.57
Pickering	Dep	10.20	11.20	13.20	14.20	15.20	16.20
Levisham	Arr	10.37	11.37	13.37	14.37	15.37	16.37
Levisham	Dep	10.40	11.40	13.40	14.40	15.40	16.40
Newtondale		10.51	11.51	13.51	14.51	15.51	16.51
Goathland	Arr	11.06	12.06	14.06	15.06	16.06	17.06
Goathland	Dep	11.10	12.10	14.10	15.10	16.10	17.10
Grosmont	Arr	11.20	12.20	14.20	15.20	16.20	17.20

M
Includes
'The Moorlander'
lunch train.

TABLE B OPERATES
April 2nd, 9th, 23rd,
30th. May 14th, 21st.
June 4th, 11th, 25th.
July 9th, 16th.
September 3rd, 10th,
24th.

TABLE C

					M				
Grosmont	Dep	09.50	10.50	11.50	12.50	13.50	14.50	15.50	16.50
Goathland	Arr	10.05	11.05	12.05	13.05	14.05	15.05	16.05	17.05
Goathland	Dep	10.10	11.10	12.10	13.10	14.10	15.10	16.10	17.10
Newtondale		10.25	11.25	12.25	13.25	14.25	15.25	16.25	17.25
Levisham	Arr	10.36	11.36	12.36	13.36	14.36	15.36	16.36	17.36
Levisham	Dep	10.40	11.40	12.40	13.40	14.40	15.40	16.40	17.40
Pickering	Arr	10.57	11.57	12.57	13.57	14.57	15.57	16.57	17.57
Pickering	Dep	10.20	11.20	12.20	13.20	14.20	15.20	16.20	17.20
Levisham	Arr	10.37	11.37	12.37	13.37	14.37	15.37	16.37	17.37
Levisham	Dep	10.40	11.40	12.40	13.40	14.40	15.40	16.40	17.40
Newtondale		10.51	11.51	12.51	13.51	14.51	15.51	16.51	17.51
Goathland	Arr	11.06	12.06	13.06	14.06	15.06	16.06	17.06	18.06
Goathland	Dep	11.10	12.10	13.10	14.10	15.10	16.10	17.10	18.10
Grosmont	Arr	11.20	12.20	13.20	14.20	15.20	16.20	17.20	18.20

M: Sundays includes 'The Moorlander' lunch train.

TABLE C OPERATES
April 16th/17th, May 7th/8th, 28th–31st, June 1st, 17th/18th.
July 1st/2nd, 22nd–27th, 30th/31st. August 1st–3rd, 6th–10th, 13th–17th, 20th–24th, 27th–31st, September 16th/17th. October 7th/8th, 28th/29th.

WINE & DINE
'Pickering Pullman' – from Pickering Friday evenings June 2nd–September 29th.
'The North Yorkshireman' – from Grosmont Saturday evenings May 6th–September 30th.
'The Moorlander' – Sunday lunches from Grosmont April 2nd–October 29th.

1995 SPECIAL EVENTS

Open Weekend	
Season Preview	April 1st/2nd
VE Wartime Weekend	May 6th–8th
Friends of *Thomas the Tank Engine*	June 17th/18th
150th Anniversary Gala	July 1st/2nd
Teddy Bears' Picnic	July 9th
Vintage Vehicle Weekend	July 22nd/23rd
Friends of *Thomas the Tank Engine*	September 16th/17th
Autumn Steam Gala	October 7th/8th
Wartime Weekend	October 28th/29th.

FARES
Adults £8.50, Child £4.30
Family £19.90

Length of operating line 18 miles

18 Steam Locos, 13 Diesels

1995 LOCOS
Repton, Eric Treacy, Q7, *Dame Vera Lynn*, 90775, USA class 5160, 75014

BED & BREAKFAST
Pickering T.I.C.
01751 473791

Lineside photographic passes £25.00 per year (limited issue).
Applications in writing to Operations Manager c/o Grosmont Station.

One of the best preserved lines in the country, crossing 20 miles of North Yorkshire Moors National Park, the line is currently enjoying the tourists' attentions centred on Goathland, aka Aidensfield in TV's *Heartbeat*.

FACILITIES
Souvenir Shop, Light Refreshments, Full Meals, On-Train Buffet, Museum, Disabled Toilet, Picnic Sites, Car Park, Railway Trail on North York Moors National Park, Schools Advice.

Paignton & Dartmouth Steam Railway

Devon

'The Nation's Holiday Line'

STANDARD GAUGE

HEADQUARTERS
Queens Park Station, Torbay Road, Paignton, Devon, TQ4 6AF

PRINCIPAL STATIONS
Paignton, Goodrington, Churston, Kingswear

HOW TO GET THERE
Road: A385 to Paignton from Totnes
Bus: Devon General Services
Rail: Paignton (adjacent)

☎ Information 01803 555872 Enquiries 01803 557360 Fax 01803 664313

TIMES

TABLE A — STANDARD SERVICE

		B	B	B	
Paignton	Dep	10.30	12.15	14.15	16.15
Goodrington	Dep	10.35	12.20	14.20	16.20
Churston	Dep	10.45	12.30	14.30	16.30
Kingswear	Arr	11.00	12.45	14.45	16.45
Kingswear	Dep	11.15	12.55	15.15	17.00
Churston	Dep	11.30	13.10	15.30	17.15
Goodrington	Dep	11.40	13.20	15.40	17.25
Paignton	Arr	11.45	13.25	15.45	17.30

All trains carry Pullman Observation Saloon at Supplementary Fare.

B: Boat Train Service.

TABLE B — MID SEASON SERVICE

		B	B	B		
Paignton	Dep	10.15	11.35	13.30	14.50	16.15
Goodrington	Dep	10.20	11.40	13.35	14.55	16.20
Churston	Dep	10.30	11.50	13.45	15.05	16.30
Kingswear	Arr	10.45	12.05	14.00	15.20	16.45
Kingswear	Arr	10.55	12.15	14.10	15.30	17.00
Churston	Dep	11.10	12.30	14.25	15.45	17.15
Goodrington	Dep	11.20	12.40	14.35	15.55	17.25
Paignton	Arr	11.25	12.45	14.40	16.00	17.30

All trains carry Pullman Observation Saloon at Supplementary Fare.

B: Boat Train Service.

TABLE A OPERATES
April 11th. Tuesdays, Thursdays, Sundays in April. Daily in May except 8th, 29th, 30th. June daily until 19th. July weekends. August weekends except 5th/6th. September 8th–October 1st, then Tuesdays, Thursdays, Sundays in October until 29th.

TABLE B OPERATES
April 16th/17th. June 20th–21st July. September 4th–8th.

TABLE C   PEAK SEASON SERVICE

		B	B	B	B	B				
Paignton	Dep	10.15	11.00	11.45	12.30	14.00	14.45	15.30	16.15	17.00
Goodrington	Dep	10.20	11.05	11.50	12.35	14.05	14.50	15.35	16.20	17.05
Churston	Dep	10.35	11.20	12.05	12.50	14.20	15.05	15.50	16.35	17.15
Kingswear	Arr	10.50	11.35	12.20	13.05	14.35	15.20	16.05	16.50	17.30

		B	B	B	B	B				
Kingswear	Dep	10.15	11.00	11.45	12.30	14.00	14.45	15.30	16.15	17.00
Churston	Dep	10.35	11.20	12.05	12.50	14.20	15.05	15.50	16.35	17.15
Goodrington	Dep	10.45	11.30	12.15	13.00	14.30	15.15	16.00	16.45	17.25
Paignton	Arr	10.50	11.35	12.20	13.05	14.35	15.20	16.05	16.50	17.30

Pullman Observation Saloon runs in certain trains.   B: Boat Train Service.

TABLE C OPERATES
Monday–Friday only – July 24th–September 1st.

The above 3 tables do not cover every possible date – please ring for confirmation.

Boat Trains: Connect with passenger ferry at Kingswear (for Dartmouth) for one hour
circular cruise round harbour.

1995 SPECIAL EVENTS

Childrens' Weekend	April 16th/17th
Thomas the Tank Engine	August 6th/7th
Santa Trains	December 3rd
	9th/10th, 16th/17th,
	23rd-24th.

CLASS 50 runs Saturdays April 29th, May 27th, June 24th, July 29th, in addition to regular steam service.

FARES
Not yet agreed

Length of operating line 7 miles

6 Steam Locos, 4 Diesels

1995 LOCOS
4588, 6435, 4920 –
Dumbleton Hall, 5239 *Goliath*
Flying Scotsman – visiting in
July & August

WINE & DINE
'Riviera Belle' Friday & Saturday evenings, Sunday lunch, Charter Hire.
Telephone for operating dates.

Grab your seat in the ex-'Devon Belle' Observation Car, pay your supplement and travel pure Great Western Railway style – by the seaside! From Paignton you skirt sandy beaches, dive under tunnels, cross viaducts and down to the historic town of Dartmouth, via Kingswear.

FACILITIES
Car Parking (no facilities at Paignton Station), Light Refreshments, Disabled and Nursing Mother Facilities at Paignton, Souvenir Shop.

Peak Rail

Derbyshire

HEADQUARTERS
Matlock Station, Matlock, Derbyshire, DE4 3NA
PRINCIPAL STATIONS
Matlock, Darley Dale
HOW TO GET THERE
Road: Matlock is on the A6
Bus: National Bus to Matlock
Rail: Matlock (not Sundays)

☎ Information 01629 580381

TIMES

Darley Dale   12.00 13.00 14.00 15.00

It has not been possible for Peak Rail to provide a full timetable as the current extension northwards continues.

Trains run Easter, then Sundays throughout the year.
Saturdays April 29th–September 30th.
Wednesdays & Thursdays July 19th–September 7th.

1995 SPECIAL EVENTS
Thomas the Tank Engine Weekend
April 8th/9th.

Length of operating line 2½ miles currently

1995 LOCOS
Warrington, The Duke

Peak Rail,as the name suggests,intend to reopen the complete line from Matlock to Buxton,taking the traveller right through the heart of the Peak District National Park.The present stretch is from Matlock (Riverside) to Darley Dale,but this line has the potential to be up in the 'Top Ten' of steam lines once the project is complete.It is recommended that intending travellers phone for timetable confirmation.

FACILITIES
Souvenir Shop, Light Refreshments, Car Park, Shop & Buffet at Darley Dale.

Pontypool & Blaenavon Railway

Gwent

HEADQUARTERS
Council Offices, High Street, Blaenavon, Gwent
PRINCIPAL STATIONS
Furnace Sidings, Whistle Inn
HOW TO GET THERE
Road: From Blaenavon follow signs to Big Pit Mining Museum
Bus: From Newport to Blaenavon (Stagecoach)
Rail: Abergavenny, 5 miles, Pontypool Rd, 5 miles, Newport, 15 miles

☎ 01495 792263

TIMES Frequent Intervals from12.00 to 17.00

SERVICE OPERATES
April 15th–17th then every Sunday until August 27th.
Bank Holidays until August 28th.
Bank Holiday weekends Saturdays until August 26th.

1995 SPECIAL EVENTS
Easter Bunny Specials April 15th/16th.
Friends of *Thomas the Tank Engine* September 2nd/3rd (provisional)

FARES
Adults £1.70, Child 80p

1995 LOCO
0–6–0 *The Lady Armaghdale* Length of operating line ¾ mile

This railway forms part of the attractions of the Big Pit Mining Museum complex, a museum
of mining in a closed coal mine.
Several ex-GWR locos on display.

FACILITIES – Souvenir Shop, Light Refreshments, Car Park.

'The Railway Age' Crewe

Cheshire

HEADQUARTERS
Crewe Heritage Centre, Vernon Way, Crewe, CW1 2BB

PRINCIPAL STATION
Site focussed around old North Junction Signal Box

HOW TO GET THERE

Road: M6 Junction 16, then A500/A5020. Signposted in town centre
Rail: Crewe, ½ mile
Bus: ¼ mile from Crewe Bus Station

☎ 01270 212130

TIMES
10.00–16.00 Daily Easter to Christmas

FARES
Museum Admission
Adult £3.00, Child £1.50, Family £7.50
Concession £2.50

Friends of *Thomas the Tank Engine* events held.

LOCOS
2 Steam Locos, 12 Diesels. Various steam locos expected through 1995 as centre is used as steam depot for services to Carlisle, Holyhead, Gloucester & Mid-Wales. Many of Pete Waterman's preserved locos are based here.

FACILITIES

Light Refreshments, Tea Room in last remaining portion of aborted Advanced Passenger Train, Mother & Baby Room, Exhibition Hall, Model Railway, Car Park, part of larger complex on Crewe History including Rolls Royce etc. Footplate Courses.

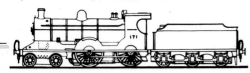

RAILWAY PRESERVATION SOCIETY
OF IRELAND

Co.Antrim

IRISH STANDARD GAUGE

HEADQUARTERS
Whitehead Excursion Station, Castleview Road, Whitehead, Co. Antrim, BT36 6HJ
PRINCIPAL STATION
Whitehead (Excursion)
HOW TO GET THERE
Road: Whitehead
Bus: Ulsterbus to Whitehead
Rail: Whitehead, ¼ mile

The Railway Preservation Society of Ireland maintains nine locomotives and carriages of varying vintage from its Whitehead base. The Society is well known for its public railtour trains, covering all parts of Ireland.

   Information/Fax 01960 353567 for latest details on any operation

1995 PROGRAMME

Easter Bunny Shuttles	April 17th
Dublin to Maynooth or Wicklow	May 6th
Bangor Belle – from Belfast	May 6th
Positioning Tour – Whitehead–Dundalk	May 13th
Dublin–Cork International Railtour	May 20th–22nd
Belfast–Derry	June 10th
Belfast–Portrush	July 15th/19th, August 12th/16th
Dublin–Enniscorthy	July 8th
Dublin–Wexford	July 29th/August 19th
BelfastvLondonderry	September 16th
Santa Specials	December

All tours are provisional until confirmed by official announcement notice.

TOUR ENQUIRIES
RPSI c/o 22 Town Lane, Islandmagee, Larne, BT40 3SZ

9 Steam Locos

1995 LOCOS

No. 461 – (Dublin & South Eastern Railway) 2–6–0
No. 171 – (Great Northern Railway of Ireland) 4–4–0 *Slieve Gullion*
No. 85 v (Great Northern Railway of Ireland) 4–4–0 *Merlin*

FACILITIES

Souvenir Shop, Light Refreshments, Licensed Bar, On-Train Buffet, Museum, Car Park, Disabled Carriage Access.

Ravenglass & Eskdale Railway

Cumbria

HEADQUARTERS
Ravenglass & Eskdale Railway Co. Ltd, Ravenglass, Cumbria, CA18 1SW
PRINCIPAL STATIONS
Ravenglass, Muncaster Mill, Irston Road, The Green, Eskdale (Dalegarth)
HOW TO GET THERE
Road: A595 between Barrow and Whitehaven
Rail: Ravenglass, 200 yards

 Enquiries 01229 717171 Fax 01229 717011 Tourist Info 01229 717270

TIMES

Trains depart Ravenglass 10.00–17.00. 40 minutes journey.
Daily from April to October and December 26th–January 1st 1996.
Weekends only in winter except December 23rd/24th.

1995 SPECIAL EVENTS

Museum Event	May 6th–8th
Family Day	May 27th
Friends of *Thomas*	
the Tank Engine	October 21st/22nd

BED & BREAKFAST
Roseyarth	01229 717275
Pennington Arms	01229 717222
Holly House	01229 717230

FARES

Adults £5.70, Child £2.90
Family 'Eskdale Explorer' Ticket
includes Railway Museum &
unlimited travel for the day £14.30

6 Steam Locos, 6 Diesels

1995 LOCOS
River Esk, River Irt, River Mite.
Bonnie Dundee, Northern Rock.

Easy to get to from the Cumbrian coast line, this is one of the best 15" gauge lines in the country. Not just scenic, it is also one of our true 'public service' railways, yet opened originally to serve a a group of iron mines in Eskdale. *River Irt* is probably the oldest 15" gauge locomotive in active service anywhere. The railway has its own loco and coach building workshops, some built for export.

FACILITIES

Souvenir Shop, Light Refreshments, Full Meals, Licensed Bar, Museum,
Disabled Facilities, Picnic Site, Car Park.

One of the highlights of steam in 1995 is the proposed running of No. 15 *Caledonia* on the Snaefell Mountain Railway, Isle of Man, as part of the line's centenary celebrations. *Caledonia* helped build the line a century ago

Colin Tyson

S15 No. 30841 at Grosmont Station, North Yorkshire Moors Railway – one of the later batch of S15s built for the Southern Railway

Eric Sawford

ROMNEY HYTHE & DYMCHURCH RAILWAY

The World's Smallest Public Railway NARROW GAUGE

HEADQUARTERS
New Romney Station, New Romney, Kent, TN28 8PL

PRINCIPAL STATIONS
Hythe, Dymchurch, New Romney, Dungeness

HOW TO GET THERE
Road: Approx 3 miles from M20 Junction 11 (Hythe turning)
Bus: From Ashford, Canterbury, Hastings, Rye, Folkestone
Rail: Folkestone Central, 5 miles

☎ Information 01797 362353 Fax 01797 365591

TIMES

TABLE A

Hythe	Dep	10.30	12.00	14.00	15.20	16.45	18.00
Dymchurch	Dep	10.48	12.18	14.18	15.38	17.03	18.18
J Stone Lane	Dep	10.53	12.23	14.23	15.43	17.08	18.23
New Romney	Arr	11.05	12.35	14.35	15.55	17.20	18.35
New Romney	Dep	11.08	12.38	14.38	15.58	-- --	-- --
Romney Sands	Dep	11.20	12.50	14.50	16.10	-- --	-- --
Dungeness	Arr	11.35	13.05	15.05	16.25	-- --	-- --
Dungeness	Dep	-- --	-- --	12.05	13.35	15.25	16.50
Romney Sands	Dep	-- --	-- --	12.20	13.50	15.40	16.05
New Romney	Arr	-- --	-- --	12.33	14.03	15.53	16.18
New Romney	Dep	09.35	11.05	12.38	14.05	15.55	16.20
J Stone Lane	Dep	09.43	11.13	12.43	14.13	16.03	16.28
Dymchurch	Dep	09.50	11.20	12.50	14.20	16.10	16.35
Hythe	Arr	10.10	11.40	13.10	14.40	16.30	16.55

TABLE A OPERATES Spring & Autumn Saturdays & Sundays (also October 23rd–27th).
Runs Saturdays & Sundays only March 4th to April 2nd & October 7th to 15th.
Also runs daily April 24th–May 5th, May 9th–26th, Sept 25th–Oct 1st & Oct 21st–29th.

TABLE B Runs Mondays to Fridays on the daily dates shown above.

Hythe	Dep	11.15	14.30	17.30
Dymchurch	Dep	11.33	14.48	17.48
J Stone Lane	Dep	11.38	14.53	17.53
New Romney	Arr	11.50	15.05	18.05
New Romney	Dep	11.53	15.08	-- --
Romney Sands	Dep	12.05	15.20	-- --
Dungeness	Arr	12.20	15.35	-- --
Dungeness	Dep	-- --	12.50	16.05
Romney Sands	Dep	-- --	13.05	16.20
New Romney	Arr	-- --	13.18	16.33
New Romney	Dep	10.00	13.20	16.35
J Stone Lane	Dep	10.08	13.28	16.43
Dymchurch	Dep	10.15	13.35	16.50
Hythe	Arr	10.35	13.55	17.10

TABLE C Early & Late Season

Hythe	Dep	10.30	11.30	12.30	13.30	14.30	15.30	16.30	17.30	18.15
Dymchurch	Dep	10.48	11.48	12.48	13.48	14.48	15.48	16.48	17.48	18.33
J Stone Lane	Dep	10.53	11.53	12.53	13.53	14.53	15.53	16.53	17.53	18.38
New Romney	Arr	11.05	12.05	13.05	14.05	15.05	16.05	17.05	18.05	18.50
New Romney	Dep	11.08	12.08	13.08	14.08	15.08	16.08	-- --	18.08A	-- --
Romney Sands	Dep	11.20	12.20	13.20	14.20	15.20	16.20	-- --	18.20A	-- --
Dungeness	Arr	11.35	12.35	13.35	14.35	15.35	16.35	-- --	-- --	-- --
Dungeness	Dep	-- --	-- --	-- --	12.05	13.05	14.05	15.05	16.05	17.05
Romney Sands	Dep	-- --	10.20	-- --	12.20	13.20	14.20	15.20	16.20	17.20
New Romney	Arr	-- --	10.33	-- --	12.33	13.33	14.33	15.33	16.33	17.33
New Romney	Dep	09.35	10.35	11.35	12.35	13.35	14.35	15.35	16.35	17.35
J Stone Lane	Dep	09.43	10.43	11.43	12.43	13.43	14.43	15.43	16.43	17.43
Dymchurch	Dep	09.50	10.50	11.50	12.50	13.50	14.50	15.50	16.50	17.50
Hythe	Arr	10.10	11.10	12.10	13.10	14.10	15.10	16.10	17.10	18.10

TABLE C OPERATES
Daily April 8th–13th, 18th–23rd.June 4th–July 25th. September 3rd–24th.

TABLE D High Season Service

Hythe	Dep	10.20	11.05	11.50	12.35	13.20	14.05 ➤
Dymchurch	Dep	10.38	11.23	12.08	12.53	13.38	14.23 ➤
J Stone Lane	Dep	10.43	11.28	12.13	12.58	13.43	14.28
New Romney	Arr	10.55	11.40	12.25	13.10	13.55	14.40
New Romney	Dep	10.58	11.43	12.28	13.13	13.58	14.43
Romney Sands	Dep	11.10	11.55	12.40	13.25	14.10	14.55
Dugeness	Arr	11.25	12.10	12.55	13.40	14.25	15.10

➤Hythe	Dep	14.50	15.35	16.20	17.05	17.30	18.15
➤Dymchurch	Dep	15.08	15.53	16.38	17.23	17.48	18.33
J Stone Lane	Dep	15.13	15.58	16.43	17.28	17.53	18.38
New Romney	Arr	15.25	16.10	16.55	17.40	18.05	18.50
New Romney	Dep	15.28	16.13	16.58	-- --	18.08A	-- --
Romney Sands	Dep	15.40	16.25	17.10	-- --	18.20A	-- --
Dungeness	Arr	15.55	16.40	17.25	-- --	-- --	-- --

Dungeness	Dep	-- --	-- --	-- --	-- --	11.40	12.25 ➤
Romney Sands	Dep	-- --	-- --	10.40	-- --	11.55	12.40 ➤
New Romney	Arr	-- --	-- --	10.53	-- --	12.08	12.53
New Romney	Dep	09.25	10.10	10.55	11.40	12.10	12.55
J Stone lane	Dep	09.33	10.18	11.03	11.48	12.18	13.03
Dymchurch	Dep	09.40	10.25	11.10	11.55	12.25	13.10
Hythe	Arr	10.00	10.45	11.30	12.15	12.45	13.30

➤Dungeness	Dep	13.10	13.55	14.40	15.25	16.10	16.55	17.40
➤Romney Sands	Dep	13.25	14.10	14.55	15.40	16.25	17.10	17.55
New Romney	Arr	13.38	14.23	15.08	15.53	16.38	17.23	18.08
New Romney	Dep	13.40	14.25	15.10	15.55	16.40	17.25	18.10
J Stone Lane	Dep	13.48	14.33	15.18	16.03	16.48	17.33	18.18
Dymchurch	Dep	13.55	14.40	15.25	16.10	16.55	17.40	18.25
Hythe	Arr	14.15	15.00	15.45	16.30	17.15	18.00	18.45

Note A – Runs if required by return ticket holders from Romney Sands.

TABLE D OPERATES
Daily April 14th–17th. May 6th–8th, 27th–June 3rd & July 26th–September 2nd.

TABLE E

Hythe	Dep	13.20	14.05	14.20	15.20	16.20	16.40	17.30	18.15
Dymchurch	Dep	13.38	-- --	14.38	15.38	16.38	16.58	17.48	18.33
J Stone Lane	Dep	13.43	-- --	14.43	15.43	16.43	17.03	17.53	18.38
New Romney	Arr	13.55	-- --	14.55	15.55	16.55	17.15	18.05	18.50
New Romney	Dep	13.58	-- --	14.58	15.58	16.58	-- --	18.08B	-- --
Romney Sands	Dep	14.10	-- --	15.10	16.10	17.10	-- --	18.20B	-- --
Dungeness	Arr	14.25	14.50	15.25	16.25	17.25	-- --	18.35B	-- --

Dungeness	Dep	14.55	15.35	15.55	16.55	17.40
Romney sands	Dep	15.10	-- --	16.10	17.10	17.55
New Romney	Arr	15.23	-- --	16.23	17.23	18.08
New Romney	Dep	15.25	-- --	16.25	17.25	18.10
J Stone Lane	Dep	15.33	-- --	16.33	17.33	18.18
Dymchurch	Dep	15.40	-- --	16.40	17.40	18.25
Hythe	Arr	16.00	16.20	17.00	18.00	18.45

Note B: Runs if required by return ticket holders from Romney Sands or Dungeness.

TABLE E OPERATES
Runs Saturdays only in Table D periods.

1995 SPECIAL EVENTS

Steam & Diesel Gala	May 14th
New Romney Bus Rally	June 18th
Friends of *Thomas the Tank Engine*	September 10th
Santa Specials	December.

BED & BREAKFAST

Broadacre	01797 362381
Waterside	01303 872253
Blue Dolphin	01797 363224

FARES

Adult £7.70, Child £3.85.
(Valid for Day)

Length of operating line 13½ miles

11 Steam Locos, 2 Diesels incl. *Hurricane, Samson, Dr Syn, Southern Maid, Green Goddess,ZZP The Bug, Typhoon.*
All locos available 1995.

Opened in 1927, this line has seen wartime use, and – at 15" gauge on one of the flattest locations in England – eliminates the need for a lineside photographic pass! A true public service railway with locos based on the A1 class engines designed by Sir Nigel Gresley, so there is a distinct LNER flavour about the line. The line's diesels found fame by hauling a 54 coach train non-stop for 11 miles in 1993 – a record indeed.

FACILITIES

Souvenir Shop, Light Refreshments, Full Meals, Licensed Bar, On-Train Buffet, Museum, Disabled Facilities, Picnic Site, Car Park.

Rudyard Lake Railway

Staffs

HEADQUARTERS
Rudyard Old Station, Leek, Staffordshire, ST13 8PF
PRINCIPAL STATIONS
Rudyard, The Dam, Lakeside, Hunthouse Wood
HOW TO GET THERE
Road: A523 Macclesfield-Leek, then B5331
Bus: Manchester–Derby GM Buses
Rail: Stoke-on-Trent, 8 miles.

 Information 01260 272862

TIMES

TABLE A

Rudyard (car park)	Dep	13.40	14.20	15.00	15.40	16.20	17.00
The Dam	Dep	13.43	14.23	15.03	15.43	16.23	17.03
Lakeside	Dep	13.47	14.27	15.07	15.47	16.27	17.07
Hunt House Wood	Arr	13.55	14.35	15.15	15.55	16.35	17.15
Hunt House Wood	Dep	14.00	14.40	15.20	16.00	16.40	17.20
Lakeside	Dep	14.05	14.45	15.25	16.05	16.45	17.25
The Dam	Dep	14.09	14.29	15.29	16.09	16.49	17.27
Rudyard	Arr	14.12	14.52	15.32	16.12	16.52	17.32

SERVICE OPERATES
Saturdays March to October and weekdays during school holidays.
On Sundays and Bank Holidays, March to October, additional return trains depart
Rudyard at 12.20 and 17.40.

Length of operating line 1½ miles

2 Steam Locos, 2 Diesels, 1 Petrol Loco

FARES
Adults £1.50, Child £1.00

1995 LOCOS
No. 6 *River Churnet* – Steam 10¼" gauge
No. 5 *Rudyard Lady* – Diesel

FACILITIES – Car Park, Picnic Site.

Rutland Railway Museum

Leics

STANDARD GAUGE

HEADQUARTERS
Cottesmore Iron Ore Mine Sidings, Ashwell Rd, Cottesmore,
Rutland, LE15 7BX

HOW TO GET THERE
Road: A1, then B668 to Cottesmore
Bus: Bartons
Rail: Oakham, 4 miles

☎ Information 01572 813203

TIMES
11.00–17.00.
Open for viewing most weekends with diesel hauled train rides on request (site conditions permitting). Admission is free – donation requested.

STEAM DATES
April 16th/17th. May 7th/8th, 28th/29th. August 26th (prov), 27th/28th, September 24th. December 3rd, 10th, 17th (Santa Specials).

ADMISSION (incl. Train ride) on steam dates.
Adult £2.50, Child £1.50, OAP £1.00, Family £6.50

The museum is dedicated to telling the story of railways in industry, especially local ironstone quarrying.

14 Steam Locos, 20 Diesels

1995 LOCOS
Include 0–4–0 ST *Singapore* – returning from Duxford mid-August.
0–4–0 ST *Dora*, 0–6–0 ST *Salmon*.
Last surving coach from Wisbech & Upwell Tramway.

FACILITIES
Souvenir Shop, Light Refreshments, Picnic Site, Car Park, Lineside Walkway, Visitor Centre.

Shropshire
Hereford & Worcester

'Britain's Premier Steam Railway'

HEADQUARTERS
The Railway Station, Bewdley, Worcester, DY12 1BG
PRINCIPAL STATIONS
Bridgnorth, Highley, Arley, Bewdley, Kidderminster Town
HOW TO GET THERE
Road: Kidderminster is on the A448 Kidderminster–Bromsgrove road.
Bewdley is off the B4195 Stourport road.
Bridgnorth is off the A458 Birmingham–Shrewsbury road
Rail: Kidderminster (adjacent)

 Information 01299 401001 Enquiries 01299 403816 Fax 01299 400839

TIMES

TABLE A

Kidderminster	Dep	-- --	10.45	12.45	14.45	16.45
Bewdley	Arr	-- --	10.56	12.56	14.56	16.56
Bewdley	Dep	-- --	10.58	12.58	14.58	16.58
Arley	Arr	-- --	11.11	13.11	15.11	17.11
Arley	Dep	-- --	11.13	13.13	15.13	17.13
Highley	Arr	-- --	11.21	13.21	15.21	17.21
Highley	Dep	-- --	11.22	13.22	15.22	17.22
Hampton Loade	Arr	-- --	11.30	13.30	15.30	17.30
Hampton Loade	Dep	-- --	11.31	13.31	15.31	17.31
Bridgnorth	Arr	-- --	11.48	13.48	15.48	17.48
Bridgnorth	Dep	10.35	12.35	14.35	16.35	-- --
Hampton Loade	Arr	10.52	12.52	14.52	16.52	-- --
Hampton Loade	Dep	10.53	12.53	14.53	16.53	-- --
Highley	Arr	11.01	13.01	15.01	17.01	-- --
Highley	Dep	11.02	13.02	15.02	17.02	-- --
Arley	Arr	11.10	13.10	15.10	17.10	-- --
Arley	Dep	11.14	13.14	15.14	17.14	-- --
Bewdley	Arr	11.27	13.27	15.27	17.27	-- --
Bewdley	Dep	11.29	13.29	15.29	17.29	-- --
Kidderminster	Arr	11.41	13.41	15.41	17.41	-- --

TABLE A OPERATES
April 14th, 19th–21st. May 9th–12th, 15th–19th, 22nd–26th.
June 5th–9th, 12th–16th, 19th–23rd, 26th–30th. July 3rd–7th, 10th–14th.
September 4th–8th, 11th–15th, 18th–22nd, 25th–29th.
October 23rd–27th. November 4th/5th, 11th/12th, 18th/19th, 25th/26th.

TABLE B

Kidderminster	Dep	10.25	11.45	13.00 (RV)	14.15	15.30	16.45 (CT)
Bewdley	Arr	10.36	11.56	13.11	14.26	15.41	16.56
Bewdley	Dep	10.45	12.00	13.15	14.30	15.45	17.00
Arley	Arr	10.58	12.13	13.28	14.43	15.58	17.13
Arley	Dep	11.00	12.16	13.31	14.46	16.01	17.14
Highley	Arr	11.08	12.24	13.39	14.54	16.11	17.22
Highley	Dep	11.10	12.26	13.41	14.56	16.11	17.23
Hampton Loade	Arr	11.18	12.34	13.49	15.04	16.19	17.31
Hampton Loade	Dep	11.21	12.37	13.52	15.07	16.22	17.34
Bridgnorth	Arr	11.38	12.54	14.09	15.24	16.39	17.51

Bridgnorth	Dep	11.00	12.15	13.30 (CT)	14.45	16.00	17.15
Hampton Loade	Arr	11.17	12.32	13.47	15.02	16.17	17.32
Hampton Loade	Dep	11.20	12.35	13.50	15.03	16.20	17.35
Highley	Arr	11.28	12.43	13.58	15.13	16.28	17.43
Highley	Dep	11.30	12.45	14.00	15.15	16.30	17.45
Arley	Arr	11.38	12.53	14.08	15.23	16.38	17.53
Arley	Dep	11.41	12.56	14.11	15.26	16.41	17.54
Bewdley	Arr	11.54	13.09	14.24	15.39	16.54	18.07
Bewdley	Dep	11.58	13.13	14.28	15.43	16.58	18.11
Kidderminster	Arr	12.09	13.24	14.39	15.54	17.09	18.22

(12.15) Departs Sundays only (+ return) 'Severn Valley Limited' lunch.

NOTES:
R: 'Severn Valley Limited' luncheon March 13th–October 30th Sundays.
RV: 'Severn Valley Venturer'– each Sunday & B.H.
CT: Cream Teas, Sundays, B.H.

TABLE B OPERATES
April 2nd,18th, 23rd, 30th. May 7th, 14th, 21st, 30th, 31st. June 1st/2nd, 11th, 18th. July 2nd, 9th, 16th–21st, 24th–28th, 31st.
Daily in August except 5th/6th, 12th/13th, 19th/20th, 26th–28th.
September 1st, 10th, 17th. October 1st, 15th, 22nd, 29th.

TABLE C Saturdays Only

Kidderminster	Dep	09.45	10.30 (D)	11.15	12.45	13.30 (D)	14.15	15.00	16.30	19.00 (DMU)
Bewdley	Dep	09.56	10.41	11.26	12.56	13.41	14.26	15.11	16.41	19.10
Arley	Dep	10.15	11.00	11.45	13.15	14.00	14.45	15.30	17.00	-- --
Highley	Dep	10.27	11.12	11.57	13.27	14.12	14.57	15.42	17.12	-- --
Hampton Loade	Dep	10.39	11.24	12.09	13.39	14.24	15.09	15.54	17.24	-- --
Bridgnorth	Arr	10.59	11.44	12.29	13.59	14.44	15.29	16.14	17.44	20.00

Bridgnorth	Dep	11.05	11.50 (D)	12.35	13.20	14.50 (D)	15.35	16.20	17.05	21.15 (DMU)
Hampton Loade	Dep	11.22	12.07	12.52	13.37	15.07	15.52	16.37	17.22	-- --
Highley	Dep	11.35	12.20	13.05	13.50	15.20	16.05	16.50	17.35	-- --
Arley	Dep	11.47	12.32	13.17	14.02	15.32	16.17	17.02	17.47	-- --
Bewdley	Dep	12.05	12.50	13.35	14.20	15.50	16.35	17.20	18.05	21.55
Kidderminster	Arr	12.22	13.07	13.52	14.37	16.07	16.52	17.37	18.18	22.05

NOTES: D   This train will normally be diesel-hauled or a DMU.
DMU This train will be a Diesel Multiple Unit.

TABLE C OPERATES
April 1st, 15th, 22nd, 29th. May 6th, 13th, 20th, 27th. June 10th,17th. July 1st, 8th, 15th, 22nd, 29th. August 5th, 12th, 19th, 26th.
September 9th, 16th, 30th. October 7th, 14th, 21st, 28th.

TABLE D (Peak Sundays/Bank Holidays)

			R	RV						CT	
Kidderminster	Dep	10.30	11.15	12.00	12.45	13.30	14.15	15.00	15.45	16.30	17.15
Bewdley	Arr	10.41	11.26	12.11	12.56	13.41	14.26	15.11	15.56	16.41	17.26
Bewdley	Dep	10.50	11.32	12.17	13.01	13.47	14.32	15.17	16.02	16.47	17.30
Arley	Arr	11.00	11.45	12.30	13.14	14.00	14.45	15.30	16.15	17.00	17.43
Arley	Dep	11.03	11.49	12.33	13.18	14.03	14.48	15.33	16.18	17.03	17.48
Highley	Arr	11.12	11.58	12.42	13.27	14.12	14.57	15.42	16.27	17.12	17.56
Highley	Dep	11.17	12.02	12.46	13.31	14.16	15.01	15.46	16.31	17.16	17.57
Hampton L	Arr	11.24	12.10	12.54	13.39	14.24	15.09	15.54	16.39	17.24	18.05
Hampton L	Dep	11.26	12.13	12.57	13.42	14.27	15.12	15.57	16.42	17.27	18.06
Bridgnorth	Arr	11.44	12.29	13.14	13.59	14.44	15.29	16.14	16.59	17.44	18.23

			R				CT				
Bridgnorth	Dep	11.05	11.50	12.35	13.20	14.05	14.50	15.35	16.20	17.05	17.50
Hampton L	Arr	11.22	12.07	12.52	13.37	14.22	15.07	15.52	16.37	17.22	18.07
Hampton L	Dep	11.27	12.12	12.57	13.42	14.27	15.12	15.57	16.42	17.27	18.10
Highley	Arr	11.35	12.20	13.05	13.50	14.35	15.20	16.05	16.50	17.35	18.18
Highley	Dep	11.39	12.24	13.09	13.54	14.39	15.24	16.09	16.54	17.39	18.20
Arley	Arr	11.47	12.32	13.17	14.02	14.47	15.32	16.17	17.02	17.47	18.28
Arley	Dep	11.52	12.37	13.22	14.07	14.52	15.37	16.22	17.07	17.52	18.30
Bewdley	Arr	12.05	12.50	13.35	14.20	15.05	15.50	16.35	17.20	18.05	18.43
Bewdley	Dep	12.11	12.56	13.41	14.26	15.11	15.56	16.41	17.26	18.07	18.45
Kidderminster	Arr	12.22	13.07	13.52	14.37	15.22	16.07	16.52	17.37	18.18	18.56

TABLE D OPERATES April 16th/17th. May 8th, 28th/29th. July 23rd, 30th.
August 6th, 13th, 20th, 27th/28th.
A Special Service will operate April 8th/9th. June 3rd/4th, 24th/25th.
September 2nd/3rd, 23rd/24th/.
October 8th. November 25th/26th. December – Santa Specials.

1995 SPECIAL EVENTS

Spring Steam Gala	April 8th/9th
Thomas Weekends	June 3rd/4th
	September 2nd/3rd
Forties Weekend	June 24th/25th
Autumn Steam Gala	September 23rd/24th
Vintage Vehicle Day	October 8th
Santa Specials	December
(write for details)	

FARES
On normal operating days, children 5–16 can travel for £1.00 if accompanied by an adult.
Family ticket £19.50

All Whole Line Return Tickets give unlimited travel for the day.

Special Rover Tickets – Gala Weekends.

Length of operating line 16 miles

If you have picked up this book for the first time and wondering where to go first, then the SVR is about the best place to start and introduce yourself to the wonderful world of steam railways. Impressive loco fleet, lovely country stations, splendid scenery and coaching stock. It's as if the Great Western Railway never ever died!

FACILITIES
Souvenir Shop, Light Refreshments, Full Meals, Model Railway (Bewdley), Through fares from selected BR stations, Car Parks, Picnic Area (Arley), Schools Service, Two Real Ale Bars, On-Train Buffets.

K4 Class No. 3442 *The Great Marquess* at Bewdley, heading a Kidderminster train, Severn Valley Railway

Eric Sawford

'West Country' Class No. 34027 *Taw Valley* – preserved at the Severn Valley Railway and often to be seen on mainline duties

Eric Sawford

Shanes Castle Railway

Co. Antrim

HEADQUARTERS
Shanes Castle, Antrim, Northern Ireland, BT41 4NE
PRINCIPAL STATIONS
Antrim, Shanes Castle
HOW TO GET THERE
Road: Off A6 Antrim–Randalstown
Bus: Ulsterbus–Antrim
Rail: Antrim, 1 mile

☎ Information 0849 428216

TIMES
Half hourly shuttle . April & May – Sundays/Bank Holidays. June – Wednesdays, Saturdays
& Sundays. July – August, Tuesdays–Thursdays, Saturdays, Sundays. September – Sundays.
A 1½ mile run from the edge of Antrim through woods to the ruins of Old Shane's Castle
(nature reserve).
3'0" gauge.

2 Steam Locos, 2 Diesels
FACILITIES – Souvenir Shop, Light Refreshments, Disabled Toilet, Picnic Site, Car Park.

Sittingbourne & Kemsley Light Railway

Kent

HEADQUARTERS
Postal: 85 Balmoral Road, Gillingham, Kent, ME7 4QG
PRINCIPAL STATIONS
Milton Halt, Kemsley Down
HOW TO GET THERE
Rail: Sittingbourne, ½ mile

☎ Information 01795 424899   Enquiries   01634 852672

TIMES
Milton Halt   Dep   14.15 15.00 15.45 16.30   for Kemsley Down
SERVICE OPERATES
April–October Sundays/Bank Holidays. Saturdays & Wednesdays in August.
8 Steam Locos, 2 Diesels.

This 2'6" gauge line was built as part of a paper manufacturing plant, adjacent to the track.
The locos built for the line include Bagnall/Kerr Stuart examples. Part of the line is
temporarily closed pending bridge repairs, but these pioneers of preservation will overcome.
Museum and Workshops at Kemsley Down (no road access).

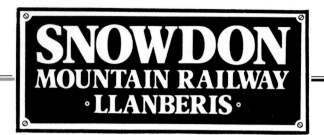

Gwynedd

NARROW GAUGE
RACK RAILWAY

HEADQUARTERS
> Llanberis, Caernarfon, Gwynedd, LL55 4TY

PRINCIPAL STATIONS
> Llanberis, Summit

HOW TO GET THERE
> Road: On A4086 Caernarfon–Capel Curig road
> Bus: from Caernarfon
> Rail: Bangor, 8½ miles

☎ Information 01286 870223 Fax 01286 872518

TIMES

Passenger trains run every day from March 15th to November 1st.

Weather permitting, and if there are at least 25 passengers, the first trains depart from Llanberis at 09.00 (08.30 in peak periods). Trains run at frequent intervals until mid–late afternoon. At peak periods, Bank Holidays and from mid-July to early September, trains are scheduled to depart from Llanberis at half hourly intervals from 08.30 to 17.00. (08.30 to 15.30 on Saturdays).

The company uses its best endeavours to run at least the 09.30, 11.30 and 13.30 trains on all service days. Trains run to summit from mid-May to mid-October, otherwise terminating at Rocky Valley/Clogwyn.

Round trip time 2 ½ hours.

Tickets are sold for a specific train time. At peak times, Reservation Tokens can be obtained from the Booking Office entitling the bearer to a place on the next available train. Tokens must be swopped for tickets 25 minutes prior to departure.

> Length of operating line approx 4½ miles

FARES
Return to Summit
£13.20 Adults
£9.50 Children
Family (2+2) on early morning
economy fare (08.30, 09.00, 09.30) £36.50

7 Steam Locos, 4 Diesels
(4 steam locos currently under repair)

Britain's only rack railway, using the 0–4–2 locos supplied new in 1896 to the line. Watch out for some new powerful diesels in '95 (to help out at busy times!).

FACILITIES

Souvenir Shop, Light Refreshments, Full Meals, Licensed Bar, Car Park.

Disabled Toilet at Llanberis and Summit. Passengers with severe mobility problems are invited to discuss requirements before visiting. Warm clothing advised. Visitors may post letters from the highest postbox in the British Isles at the Summit Café.

South Devon Railway   Devon

'The Primrose Line'   STANDARD GAUGE

HEADQUARTERS
The Station, Buckfastleigh, Devon, TQ11 0DZ

PRINCIPAL STATIONS
Buckfastleigh, Staverton, Totnes (Littlehempston Riverside)

HOW TO GET THERE
Road: Buckfastleigh is off A38 midway between Exeter and Plymouth
Bus: 165 from Totnes, x38 Exeter/Plymouth
Rail: Totnes, 4 minutes walk

SERVICE OPERATES
Wednesdays & Sundays in April & October. Tuesdays, Wednesdays, Saturdays & Sundays in May.
Daily Easter week. Daily from end of May 20th–October 8th.
October – daily half term week.

☎ Information 01364 642338 Totnes 01803 868472

TIMES

TABLE A

Buckfastleigh	Dep	11.00	12.30	14.20	15.40
Staverton	Dep	11.10	12.40	14.30	15.50
Totnes (LR)	Arr	11.25	12.55	14.45	16.05
Totnes (LR)	Dep	11.40	13.10	15.00	16.20
Staverton	Arr	11.50	13.20	15.10	16.30
Buckfastleigh	Arr	12.05	13.35	15.25	16.45

TABLE A OPERATES   On all days except those covered in Tables B & C.

TABLE B

Buckfastleigh	Dep	10.45	12.00	13.45	15.00	16.15
Staverton	Dep	11.00	12.15	14.00	15.15	16.30
Totnes (LR)	Arr	11.10	12.25	14.10	15.25	16.40
Totnes(LR)	Dep	11.20	12.35	14.20	15.35	16.50
Staverton	Arr	11.30	12.45	14.30	15.45	17.00
Buckfastleigh	Arr	11.45	13.00	14.45	16.00	17.15

TABLE B OPERATES   Sundays to Thursdays in summer holidays.

TABLE C

Buckfastleigh	Dep	10.25	11.35	12.45	13.55	15.05	16.15
Staverton	Arr	10.40	11.50	13.00	14.10	15.20	16.30
Totnes(LR)	Arr	10.50	12.00	13.10	14.20	15.30	16.40
Totnes(LR)	Dep	11.00	12.10	13.20	14.30	15.40	16.50
Staverton	Arr	11.10	12.20	13.30	14.40	15.50	17.00
Buckfastleigh	Arr	11.25	12.35	13.45	14.55	16.05	17.15

TABLE C OPERATES   April 16th/17th. May 7th/8th, 28th/29th. August 27th/28th.

1995 SPECIAL EVENTS

Easter Gala	April 16th/17th
Thomas the Tank Engine	May 7th/8th
Spring Steam Gala	May 28th/29th
Railway at War	June 17th/18th
Visit of *Locomotion No. 1*	July 16th–August 12th
Autumn Steam Gala	August 27th/28th
Vintage Vehicle Rally	September 24th
Enthusiasts' Weekend	October 14th/15th
Thomas the Tank Engine	October 22nd
Santa Specials	December

Once accused of being 'over commercial', the ex-Dart Valley line is now safely in the hands of professional volunteers and is reaping the benefits of the change in fortune.

FARES
Adult £5.60, Child £3.90
Family £16.90
(2 Adults & 2 Children)

WINE & DINE
Devonshire Pullman
Sunday Lunches - first Sunday in month & Charter Hire.

Length of operating line 7 miles

16 Steam Locos, 6 Diesels

1995 LOCOS
Errol Lonsdale, Sapper, 1369
and possibly other visiting locos.

20% reduction on Standard SDR fares on production of BR ticket at Totnes.
Western National X80 route (Torquay/Paignton/Totnes) has combined rail/coach tickets.

RIVER-RAIL

Board a 'Red Cruiser' at Dartmouth. Sail up river to Totnes, join the train, and return by the same route to Dartmouth. Alternatively board the train at Buckfastleigh and do the same trip in reverse.
Join River-Rail at Dartmouth or Buckfastleigh.
Book at Buckfastleigh Station Booking Office, or 'Red Cruiser' Kiosk on Dartmouth Embankment.
Tel 01803 832109.

Combine visit with Buckfast Butterfly Farm and Otter Sanctuary.
Few minutes walk from Station. Tel 01364 642916 (separate admission charge).

FACILITIES
Souvenir Shop, Light Refreshments, Full Meals, On-Train Buffet, Museum, Disabled Facilities, Picnic Site, Car Park.

Southport Railway Centre

Merseyside

HEADQUARTERS
Motive Power Depot, Derby Road, Southport, PR9 0TY

HOW TO GET THERE
Road: On A565, via M58/M6
Bus: Many services from Preston, Liverpool, St.Helens, Warrington
Rail: Southport, Merseyrail, ¼ mile

☎ Information 01704 530693 Fax 01704 563593

TIMES
Centre open
WINTER: January–May, September–December – weekends only 12.00–17.00.
SUMMER: June–August weekends 11.00–17.00.
WEEKDAYS: June 12.00–17.00. Closed Mondays & Fridays.
            July/August 12.00–17.00. Closed Fridays.

1995 SPECIAL EVENTS

Easter Egg Specials	April 14th–17th
Grumpy Engines' Weekend	April 29th/30th
Teddy Bear Specials	May 28th/29th
Friendly Engines' Weekend	June 10th/11th
Main Line Steam	June 24th/25th
Steam Days	July 2nd, 9th, 16th
Modellers Weekend	July 22nd/23rd
Steam Day	July 30th/August 6th
Thomas Gala	August 12th/13th
Steam Day	August 20th
Enthusiasts' Week	August 26th–28th
Diesel Day	September 10th
Halloween	October 28th/29th
Santa Trains	December weekends & 23rd

FARES
Adult £2.00,
Child & OAP £1.00,
increased for Special Events.
cheaper non steam days.

16 Steam Locos, 8 Diesels

1995 LOCOS
193 *Shropshire*, Peckett No.5,
Glasshoughton No.4
Alexander, Agecroft No.2,
St. Monans.
Some locos may visit other
centres in 1995.

Over a century old, the centre's depot is the former Lancashire & Yorkshire Railway Shed erected in 1891.

FACILITIES

Souvenir Shop, Light Refreshments, Disabled Facilities, Car Park, Party Hire Train, Museum, On-Train Buffet – Special Events Only.

South Tynedale Railway

Cumbria

'England's Highest Narrow Gauge Railway'

NARROW GAUGE

HEADQUARTERS
Alston Station, Alston, Cumbria, CA9 3JB

PRINCIPAL STATIONS
Alston, Gilderdale, Kirkhaugh (under construction)

HOW TO GET THERE
Road: A686/A689/B6277 to Alston
Bus: Wright Brothers, from Haltwhistle, 5 times daily (x Sun). Tel 01434 381200
Rail: Haltwhistle, 13 miles

☎ Information 01434 381696

TIMES

TABLE A
Alston   Dep   11.00 12.00 14.00 15.00 16.00
A OPERATES Weekdays and non-steam weekends April 1st–September 14th.

TABLE B
Alston   Dep   11.00 12.00 13.00 14.00 15.00 16.00 17.00
B OPERATES Weekends/Bank Holidays, steam traction April 14th–October 1st.

TABLE C
Alston   Dep   12.00 14.00 15.00
C OPERATES Non steam September 19th–October 27th.

SERVICE OPERATES
April – Saturdays, Sundays, Bank Holidays and daily 14th–23rd.
May – Saturdays, Sundays, Bank Holidays and 30th/31st.
June – daily except Mondays & Fridays. July – daily. August – daily.
September – daily except Mondays & Fridays.
October – Saturdays, Sundays & daily 21st–29th.
Santa Service December 9th/10th, 16th/17th, 23rd/24th.

1995 SPECIAL EVENTS
Friends of *Thomas*
the Tank Engine   May 6th-8th
                                  October 28th/29th
Teddy Bears' Day   May 31st
Transport Extravaganza   July 1st/2nd

Length of operating line 1½ miles

FARES (provisional)
Adult £2, Child £1, OAP £2.

5 Steam Locos, 10 Diesels
Naklo, 12 *Chaka's Kraal No. 6,*
14 *Helen Kathryn.*
NO vehicular acess to Gilderdale or
Kirkhaugh.

The STR may not be the most accessible of lines, but the effort is worth it, most of all for
the signalling and variety of motive power. The extension to Kirkhaugh is due to open
August 1995.

FACILITIES
Souvenir Shop, Light Refreshments, Disabled Facilities, Picnic Site, Car Park.

114

Steamtown Railway Centre

Lancs

HEADQUARTERS

Steamtown Railway Centre, Warton Road, Carnforth, Lancs, LA5 9HX

HOW TO GET THERE

Road: via M6 to Jct 35 then B6254 to town centre, signposted
Rail: Carnforth, ¾ mile

☎ Information 01524 732100 Enquiries 01524 734220

TIMES
10.00–16.00. Daily until Easter.
09.00–17.00. Daily Easter to October. Open daily except Christmas.

STEAMING DATES
Standard gauge shuttle, (¾ mile), runs Sundays, Bank Holidays & school holidays Easter to November.

Narrow gauge line operates Saturdays, Sundays, Bank Holidays & school holidays Easter to November.

FARES (incl. Admission to site)

Full Steaming Days	Adults £3.50, Child £2.30
N/G Steaming Days	Adults £2.60, Child £1.75
Static Days	Adults £2.10

Just a stone's throw from the famous *Brief Encounter* spot, lies a full size steam depot, host to many a mainline loco visit.
An impressive coaling tower, turntable and atmospheric running sheds give Steamtown that true steam shed atmosphere.

FACILITIES
Souvenir Shop, Light Refreshments, Collectors Corner, Model Railway, Museum, Car Park.

Strathspey Railway   Highlands

HEADQUARTERS
>Aviemore (Speyside) Station, Dalfaber Road, Aviemore, PH22 1PY

PRINCIPAL STATIONS
>Aviemore (Speyside), Boat of Garten

HOW TO GET THERE
>Road: A9 to Aviemore, B970 Dalfaber Road
>Bus: City Link and others
>Rail: Aviemore, ½ mile

☎ Information 01479 810725 Boat of Garten Stn 01479 831692 Fax 01479 811022

TIMES

TABLE A

Boat of Garten	Dep	10.10	11.20	12.40	14.30	15.50
Aviemore	Arr	10.30	11.40	13.00	14.50	16.10
Aviemore	Dep	10.40	12.00	13.30	15.10	16.20
Boat of Garten	Arr	11.00	12.20	13.50	15.30	16.40

SERVICE OPERATES
April 2nd, 5th, 9th, 12th–14th, 16th–19th, 23rd, 26th.
May 3rd, 7th/8th, 10th, 14th, 17th, 21st, 24th, 28th–31st.
June – daily except Saturdays. July – daily. August – daily.
September – daily except Saturdays & 24th.
October 1st/2nd, 4th, 8th, 11th, 15th–22nd, 25th, 29th.
December 17th, 26th, 31st. January 1st/2nd 1996.

APRIL 15th – 'AT HOME DAY' Extra services dep. Boat of Garten at 9.20, 13.50, 16.50 – diesel hauled.

1995 SPECIAL EVENTS
Friends of *Thomas*
the Tank Engine   April 29th/30th, May 1st,
                     September 23rd/24th. (Spl T/T)
VE-Day   May 8th
DMU Day   October 21st

BED & BREAKFAST
Heatherbrae Hotel   01479 821345
Bydand, Dulnain Bridge   01479 851278

FARES
Adults £4.20, Child £2.10, Family £10.50

Length of operating line 5 miles

9 Steam Locos, 6 Diesels
incl. ex-C.R 828, No. 9.

WINE & DINE
'Strathspey Clansman'
Wednesday lunch in July/August

This line boasts some superb scenery – even better in the snow!
We recommend Demonstration Day April 15th as your chance to see this railway at its best!

FACILITIES
Souvenir Shop, Buffet/Bar on train only, Picnic Site, Car Park, Small Exhibits Museum.

The 10.20 departure awaits the 'right away' on the first day of 1991, Boat of Garten Station, Strathspey Railway. 'Black 5' No. 5025 finds it deep and crisp and even

Colin Tyson

Caledonian Railway No. 828 hauls the 12.00 Aviemore train to Boat of Garten over Kinchurdy Bridge

G. Lumsden

Dorset

STANDARD GAUGE

HEADQUARTERS
Station House, Swanage, Dorset, BH19 1HB
PRINCIPAL STATION
Swanage, Corfe Castle
HOW TO GET THERE
Road: Centre of Swanage from A351 Wareham–Swanage Road, or
Park & Ride at Harmans Cross (between Corfe Castle & Swanage)
peak summer season.
Bus: Wilts & Dorset 142/3/4 from Wareham.
150 from Bournemouth (open top in summer). Tel 01202 673555
Rail: Wareham, 10 miles

☎ Information 01929 424276 Enquiries 01929 425800 Fax 01929 425800

TIMES
TABLE A

Swanage	Dep	11.30	12.50	14.00	15.00
Herston	Dep	11.35	12.55	14.05	15.05
Harmans Cross	Arr	11.45	13.05	14.15	15.15
Harmans Cross	Dep	12.00	13.20	14.30	15.30
Herston	Dep	12.10	13.30	14.40	15.40
Swanage	Arr	12.15	13.35	14.45	15.45

TABLE A OPERATES
March 5th, 12th, 19th, 26th. April 2nd, 9th.

TABLE B

Swanage	Dep	10.30	11.40	12.50	14.10	15.20	16.30	18.00	19.30	20.30
Herston	Dep	10.35	11.45	12.55	14.15	15.25	16.35	18.05	19.35	20.35
Harmans Cross	Arr	10.45	11.55	13.05	14.25	15.35	16.45	18.15	19.45	20.45
Harmans Cross	Dep	11.00	12.10	13.20	14.40	15.50	17.00	18.20	19.50	20.50
Herston	Dep	11.10	12.20	13.30	14.50	16.00	17.10	18.30	20.00	21.00
Swanage	Arr	11.15	12.25	13.35	14.55	16.05	17.15	18.35	20.05	21.05

TABLE B OPERATES
April 14th.

APRIL 15TH ONWARDS
It is envisaged that services will commence to Corfe Castle and Norden as from April 15th.
At time of going to press, clearance has not been given. A new timetable will only be issued
once approved, thus there is no planned timetable. Railway runs May weekends/Bank
Holidays, daily June, July, August, first week of September, then
September/October/November weekends.

FARES (up to & incl. Easter)
Adult £4.00, Child £2.00
Family £10.00
(2 Adults & up to 4 Children)
Day Rovers £5.50

Length of operating line 3 miles
(up to Easter)

6 Steam Locos, 4 Diesels

WINE & DINE
'Swanage Starlight' from April 15th. Saturday evenings. 20.00

Children's Birthday Parties (not May to September)

Swanage Booking Office is open every day except December 25th.
(BR ticket agents & Swanage Railway advance bookings)

Although track has been laid through Corfe Castle for some time now, Swanage Railway have been anxious to operate as soon as possible and it does seem that 1995 will be the year – Good Luck for Easter! The road between Wareham and Swanage can get pretty full on a summer's day, and my advice to you all is to Park and Ride at the new Norden facility and travel to Swanage with dignity!

FACILITIES
Souvenir Shop, On-Train Buffet, Museum, Disabled Access, Picnic Site, Car Park, Footplate Courses.

STEAM LINE

Mainline information updated weekly.   Make a note of our number.

0891 88 1968

Main Line Steam Timings – Competitions

0891

Calls cost 36p min cheap rate. 48p min all other times
(compiled by Silver Fox Pub, For Newstel Ltd, Glasgow)

Swansea Vale Railway

W. Glamorgan

STANDARD GAUGE

HEADQUARTERS
 (Postal) Upper Bank, Pentrechwyth, Swansea, W.Glamorgan, SA1 7DB

PRINCIPAL STATION
 Six Pit Junction, Nant-Y-Ffin Road, Llansamlet, Swansea

HOW TO GET THERE
 Road: M4 Jct 44, A484 to Llansamlet, A4217 to Six Pit Junction
 Rail: Llansamlet, 1½ miles, Swansea High Street, 3 miles
 Bus: South Wales Transport. Tel 01792 580580

☎ Information 01792 653615 /467045 / 581919 Fax 01792 653615

TIMES

Six Pit Jct. Dep 11.00 11.30 12.00 12.30 13.15 13.45 14.15 14.45 15.15
       Dep 15.45 16.15 16.45
       Last two departures April–August only. Nov 5th evening extras.

SERVICE OPERATES

April 14th–17th. May 6th–8th, 27th–29th. June 18th, 25th.
July 2nd, 9th, 15th/16th, 22nd/23rd, 26th, 29th/30th.
August 2nd, 5th/6th, 9th, 12th/13th,16th, 19th/20th, 23rd, 26th–28th. October 28th/29th.
November 5th. December 2nd/3rd, 9th/10th, 16th/17th.

1995 SPECIAL EVENTS

Taffy the Tank Engine   May 6th-8th
            August 26th-28th

Brake Van Rides   July 15th/16th
Ghost Trains   October 28th/29th
Santa Specials   Dec – dates above

Length of operating line ⅔ mile (public)
1½ total

5 Steam Locos, 7 Diesels

1995 LOCOS
Peckett 0–4–0 No. 1345
GWR PT 9642 early season

Extra weekday steamings for schools etc on demand.

Footplate courses and educational school steamings midweek from April.

FACILITIES
Car Park

Current line is between Six Pit Junction and Llansamlet.
Cwm Crossing and Upper Bank Junction not yet open to public.

Swindon & Cricklade Railway — Wiltshire

HEADQUARTERS
>Blunsdon Station, Tadpole Lane, Blunsdon, Nr Swindon, Wiltshire, SN2 4DZ

PRINCIPAL STATION
>Blunsdon, Hayes Knoll

HOW TO GET THERE
>Road: Blunsdon is off A419, 3 miles W. of Swindon, signposted Purton
>Bus: From Swindon (summer only)
>Rail: Swindon, 4 miles

☎ Information 01793 771615 (weekends only).   01793 750335

TIMES
>Site open every weekend for viewing with steam service operating from 11.30 to 16.00 at 30 minute intervals, on at least one weekend per month. Tel. for steaming dates.

1995 SPECIAL EVENTS

Easter Bunny Eggspress	April 16th/17th	Length of operating line 1 mile
Thomas the Tank Weekend	April 30th/May 1st	
VE-Day	May 7th	**FARES**
Postman Pat	May 28th/29th	Adults £2.50
Father's Day	June 18th	Child/OAP £1.50
Evening Steam Trains	July 22nd	
Thomas the Tank Weekend	August 27th/28th	4 Steam Locos, 3 Diesels
Steam day	September 24th	
Halloween	October 31st	**1995 LOCOS**
Santa Trains	November 26th	Peckett 0–4–0 *Merlin*
	December 3rd, 10th, 17th	Barclay 0–4–0 *Richard Trevithick*
Mince Pie Specials	January 1st 1996	Restaurant Car – available on demand

BED & BREAKFAST
Peartree Hotel   01793 772100
Marsh Farm Hotel   01793 848044

After a slow start, this line is now coming along well. The original home of the *Port Line* Locomotive Project (the loco is now at the Bluebell), the country railway station at Blunsdon is a fine restoration job.

FACILITIES
Souvenir Shop, Footplate Courses, Light Refreshments, Licensed Bar, On-Train Buffet, Disabled Facilities, Museum, Car Park, Picnic Site.

Gwynedd

HEADQUARTERS
> Wharf Station, Tywyn, Gwynedd, LL36 9EY

PRINCIPAL STATIONS
> Tywyn Wharf, Dolgoch, Abergynolwyn, Nant Gwernol

HOW TO GET THERE
> Road: A493 from Machynlleth or Dolgellau
> Bus: Bus Gwynedd, 28, 29, 30 from Machynlleth/Dolgellau
> Rail: Tywyn, 200 yds

☎ Information 01654 710472 Shop/Buffet 01654 711012 Fax 01654 711755

TIMES   (Tywyn Wharf departure times – all are return journeys)

<u>TABLE A</u>

a)   Tywyn Wharf Dep   14.00 operates Sundays only until March 26th.

b)   Tywyn Wharf Dep   11.30 14.20 operates daily April 1st–13th.

c)   Tywyn Wharf Dep   10.20 11.30 12.05 13.10 14.20 15.25
operates Easter Week from April 14th–21st.

d)   Tywyn Wharf Dep   11.30 14.20 operates April 22nd–May 26th daily.

<u>TABLE B</u>

a)   Tywyn Wharf Dep   10.20 11.30 13.10 14.20.

TABLE B OPERATES Daily May 27th–June 2nd.
(Saturdays between June 3rd–July 14th)

Sunday May 28th–Friday June 2nd is same as July 15th–September 1st
Monday to Friday Service.

TABLE C

a) Tywyn Wharf   Dep   10.00   10.40   11.30   12.30   13.20   14.20   15.10   16.00
operates Mondays to Fridays between July 15th–September 1st.
Also Sundays between May 28th–June 2nd, August 27th.

b) Tywyn Wharf   Dep   10.20   11.30   13.10   14.20   16.00
operates Saturdays & Sundays between July 15th–September 1st.
19.00 train – Sundays only.

TABLE D

a) Tywyn Wharf   Dep   10.20   11.30   13.10   14.20
operates daily between September 2nd–29th.

b) Tywyn Wharf   Dep   11.30   14.20
operates daily between September 30th– November 4th.

1995 SPECIAL EVENTS

Rolt vehicle Rally	May 27th/28th
Victorian Week	July 30th–August 5th
Race the Train	August 19th
Land Rover Rally	August 27th
Gala Day	September 30th
Santa Specials	December 9th/16th
Christmas Service	December 26th–January 1st 1996

BED & BREAKFAST
01654 711125, 711118, 711100
LINESIDE PHOTOGRAPHIC PASSES
Non Members £3.00

FARES
Adults £7.00, Child £3.50
Family £16.00 (2 Adults, 1 Child)
Family £18.00 (2 Adults, 2 Children)

1995 LOCOS
No. 1 *Talyllyn*, No. 6 *Douglas*,
No. 3 *Sir Haydn*, No. 4 *Peter Sam*,
No. 7 *Tom Rolt*

Length of operating line 7¼ miles

6 Steam Locos, 3 Diesels

The first preserved railway, over forty years ago. The Talyllyn proved that non professionals could run a railway – in fact they had a ten year head start before the first standard gauge preserved line came on the scene. The Talyllyn is a delight – lovely scenery, locos and coaches, and very well run. Author of the *Thomas* books, Rev Awdry, used to be a guard on the line in the early days – and indeed it gave him inspiration for many stories!

FACILITIES

Souvenir Shop, Light Refreshments, Museum, Disabled Facilities, Picnic Site, Car Park.

RAILWAY MAGAZINE

is the only all-encompassing railway publication the serious enthusiast will ever need. Whether it's the proud tradition of the past, the important issues of the present or the exciting prospects of the future, it's all between the covers of Railway Magazine.

Now with **MORE STEAM** and **PRESERVATION** news in every issue than ever before!

Available from all good newsagents or phone the HOTLINE 0622 721555 for money-saving subscriptions.

Tanfield Railway  Tyne & Wear

HEADQUARTERS
Tanfield Railway, Old Marley Hill, Gateshead, Tyne & Wear

PRINCIPAL STATIONS
Andrews House, Causey, Sunniside

HOW TO GET THERE
Road: Off A6076 Sunniside–Stanley Road
Bus: X30 Mondays–Saturdays, X80 Summer.
         Go-Ahead Northern 01207 232035
Rail: Newcastle, 5 miles

☎ Information 0191 274 2002

TIMES

TABLE A

								A	A	
East Tanfield	Dep	-- --	11.36	12.36	13.46	14.56	16.06	-- --	17.06	
Causey	Dep	-- --	11.44	12.44	13.54	15.04	16.14	-- --	17.14	
Andrews House	Arr	-- --	11.51	12.51	14.01	15.11	16.21	-- --	17.20	
Andrews House	Dep	11.00	12.00	13.10	14.20	15.30	-- --	16.30	-- --	
Sunniside	Arr	11.05	12.00	13.15	14.25	15.35	-- --	16.35	-- --	
								A		
Sunniside	Dep	11.11	12.11	13.21	14.31	15.41	-- --	16.41	-- --	
Andrews House	Dep	11.17	12.17	13.27	14.37	15.47	-- --	16.47	-- --	
Causey	Dep	11.25	12.25	13.35	14.45	15.55	-- --	16.55	-- --	
East Tanfield	Arr	11.30	12.30	13.40	14.50	16.00	-- --	17.00	-- --	

TABLE A OPERATES
Sundays to July 30th, Sept 3rd to Nov 26th (except B.H, Sundays, Saturdays & Mondays)

TABLE B

East Tanfield	Dep	-- --	11.36	12.36	-- --	-- --	-- --	13.36	14.16	14.56	15.36	►
Causey	Dep	-- --	11.43	12.43	-- --	-- --	-- --	13.43	14.23	15.03	15.43	►
Andrews House	Arr	-- --	11.50	12.50	-- --	-- --	-- --	13.50	14.30	15.10	15.50	
Andrews House	Dep	11.00	12.00	-- --	Z	13.40	14.20	15.00	15.40	16.20		
Sunniside	Arr	11.05	12.05	-- --	13.05	13.45	14.25	15.05	15.45	16.25		
Sunniside	Dep	11.11	12.11	-- --	13.11	13.51	14.31	15.11	15.51	16.31		
Andrews House	Dep	11.17	12.17	-- --	13.17	13.57	14.37	15.17	15.57	16.37		
Causey	Dep	11.26	12.26	-- --	13.26	14.06	14.46	15.26	16.06	16.46		
East Tanfield	Arr	11.31	12.31	-- --	13.31	14.11	14.51	15.31	16.11	16.51		

		A	A			
►East Tanfield	Dep	16.16	16.56	-- --	17.36	
►Causey	Dep	16.23	17.03	-- --	17.43	
Andrews House	Arr	16.30	17.10	-- --	17.50	
Andrews House	Dep	-- --	-- --	-- --	17.00	-- --
Sunniside	Arr	-- --	-- --	-- --	17.05	-- --
Sunniside	Dep	-- --	-- --	-- --	17.11	-- --
Andrews House	Dep	-- --	-- --	-- --	17.17	-- --
Causey	Dep	-- --	-- --	-- --	17.26	-- --
East Tanfield	Arr	-- --	-- --	-- --	17.31	-- --

NOTES:
A: See daily notices for availability.
Z: Leaves for Marley Hill.

An extra train leaves Marley Hill
at 13.00, arriving at Sunniside at
13.05 on Bank Holiday Sundays
& Mondays.

TABLE B OPERATES Bank Holiday Sundays & Mondays, also Sundays Aug 6th to Aug 27th.

1995 SPECIAL EVENTS

Coal Train Day	March 26th
	October 22nd
Teddy Bears' Day	April 2nd
	September 23rd/24th
Vintage Bus Day	May 14th
Vintage Car Day	May 21st
Small Engine Weekend	May 28th/29th
Enthusiasts' Weekend	July 1st/2nd
Children's Weekend	August 5th/6th
Big Engine Weekend	August 27th/28th
Santa Trains	December
Mince Pie Trains	December 26th/27th

FARES

Adults £3.00, Child £1.50, Family £7.50

29 Steam Locos, 11 Diesels

1995 LOCOS

No. 2, No. 20, No. 21, No. 38, *Irwell*, *Progress*, *Wellington*.

Recreating the colliery railway passenger service, travelling in 100 year old four- and six-wheeled coaches into the scenic Causey Arch Park.

FACILITIES

Souvenir Shop, Light Refreshments, Picnic Site, Car Park.

The West Somerset Railway can boast some delightful stations along its route to the sea. On a quiet February morning Crowcombe Station awaits a special traffic working to disturb the peace

Paul Appleton

126

Teifi Valley Railway

Dyfed

Green River Valley Line   NARROW GAUGE
1895–1995 CENTENARY YEAR

HEADQUARTERS
Henllan Station, Henllan, Llandysul, Dyfed, SA44 5TD
PRINCIPAL STATIONS
Henllan, Pontprenshitw, Llandyfriog
HOW TO GET THERE
Road: A484 Carmarthen–Cardigan road
Bus: Carmarthen–Cardigan service (in frequent)
Rail: Carmarthen, 14 miles

☎ Information 01559 371 077

TIMES
Henllan   Dep   11.00 12.00 13.30 14.30 15.30 16.30
Round Trip 40 minutes. 17.30 train in High Season

SERVICE OPERATES
Daily April 14th until end of October.

1995 SPECIAL EVENTS

Easter Sunday Fair	April 16th
Victorian Weekend	August 27th/28th
Halloween Specials	October 28th
Santa Trains	December 16th-24th.

1 Steam Loco, 2 Diesels
Alan George Hunslet 0–4–0.

FARES
Adults £3.50, Child £1.50, OAP £3.00

Length of operating line 2 miles

LINESIDE PHOTOGRAPHIC PASSES
£1 Members, £2 Non Members

FACILITIES
Souvenir Shop, Light Refreshments, Museum/Library, Disabled Facilities,
Picnic Site, Car Park.

Telford Steam Railway

Salop

HEADQUARTERS
Bridge Road, Horsehay, Telford, Shropshire

☎ Information 01952 503880

TIMES 11.00–16.00
Sundays & Bank Holidays from Easter until end of September plus Santa Specials.

No details received from this site, but contact details have been included. Intending visitors
should draw their own conclusions and try to contact the line before making any visits.

Vale of Rheidol Railway   Dyfed

HEADQUARTERS
>The Locomotive Shed, Park Avenue, Aberystwyth, Dyfed, SY23 1PG

PRINCIPAL STATIONS
>Aberystwyth, Devil's Bridge

HOW TO GET THERE
>Road: Aberystwyth is on the junction of A487 and A44
>Rail: Aberystwyth (adjacent)

☎ Information 01970 625819 Fax 01685 384854

TIMES

		Y	X	Y	Y	X	Y
Aberystwyth	Dep	10.45	11.00	12.15	14.00	14.30	15.45
		Y	X	Y	Y	X	Y
Devil's Bridge	Dep	12.30	13.00	14.15	16.00	16.30	17.30

NOTES:
X: Runs April 14th–20th, 22nd–27th 29th/30th. May – daily except Fridays
>June – daily. July – daily except those shown on Table Y.
>August Fridays, Saturdays & Sundays.
>September 1st–28th (except Fridays). October Tues, Weds, Thurs, Suns.

Y: Runs July 24th–27th, 31st. August Mondays to Thursdays.

FARES

Adults £10.00, Child £5.00
Two Children under 16 travel for £1.00
for each Adult paying normal fare.

Single journey time 1 hour.

Length of operating line 11¾ miles

3 Steam Locos, 1 Diesel

GWR Built 1923
Owain Glyndwr, Llywelyn, Prince of Wales.
Purpose-built for V.o.R.

The Vale of Rheidol Railway is noted for being the last steam-operated line to survive under ownership of British Rail, long after steam disappeared from the national network. Still suffering from lack of investment, the line was sold by BR in 1988, and since 1989 has been owned and operated by the Brecon Mountain Railway.

FACILITIES

Souvenir Shop, Picnic Site and Café at Devil's Bridge.
The famous Mynach Falls, Jacob's Ladder and the Devil's Punchbowl are within walking distance of the Station. Ask for directions at Booking Office.

Wells Harbour Railway

Norfolk

HEADQUARTERS
C/O Pinewoods Caravan Park, Beach Road, Wells-next-the-Sea, Norfolk

PRINCIPAL STATIONS
Wells Harbour, Pinewoods (Caravan Park)

HOW TO GET THERE
Road: On the A149, Beach Road is by the quay
Bus: Eastern Counties to Wells
Rail: Norwich or Kings Lynn, approx 20 miles

☎ Information 01328 878871

TIMES

TABLE A

	Dep										
Wells Harbour	10.50	11.30	12.10	12.50	13.25	14.30	15.10	15.50	16.30	17.10	- -*- -
Pinewoods	10.30	11.10	11.50	12.30	13.10	14.10	14.50	15.30	16.10	16.50	17.30

SERVICE OPERATES
Easter Week, then weekends only until Spring Bank Holidays.
Daily from Spring Bank Holiday until July, and from September 1st until mid-September.
Weekends only from mid-September to end of September.

TABLE B
Wells Harbour Dep 10.50 and then every 40 minutes until 18.30
Pinewoods   Dep 10.30 and then every 40 minutes until 18.30

SERVICE OPERATES
Daily from July to September. At peak times, during mid-July to end of August, services run at 15 minute intervals. Service operates late evenings in high season.

NOTES: On Table B, the last departure from Wells Harbour is 23.10 and 22.45 on Sundays. Late evening trains are subject to revision.

Length of operating line 1 mile

1 Steam Loco, 1 Petrol Loco

FARES
Single Adult 60p, Child 40p

This 10¼" gauge line connects a large caravan park with the town and harbour with surely the longest operating day of any comparable system. Combined with a trip on the Wells and Walsingham Railway, Wells must be the place for minimum gauge enthusiasts.

FACILITIES
Picnic Area, Light Refreshments, Bars, Car Parking, Beach are all within short walking distance of both stations.

Wells & Walsingham Railway

Norfolk

HEADQUARTERS
Stiffkey Road, Wells-next-the-Sea, Norfolk, NR23 1QB

PRINCIPAL STATIONS
Wells-next-the-Sea, Walsingham

HOW TO GET THERE

Road:	On A149 Cromer road
Bus:	450 from Norwich (Eastern Counties)
Rail:	Norwich, 24 miles, Kings Lynn, 22 miles

☎ Information 01328 856506

TIMES

TABLE A

Wells	Dep	10.15	11.45	13.30	15.00	16.30
Walsingham	Dep	11.00	12.30	14.15	15.45	17.15

TABLE B

Wells	Dep	10.30	12.00	14.00	15.30
Walsingaham	Dep	11.15	12.45	14.45	16.15

SERVICE OPERATES
Table A Easter week, then Spring Bank Holiday to mid-September.
Table B End of Easter week to Spring Bank Holiday.
Mid-September to September 30th. October half term week.

FARES
Adults £4.00, Child £3.50,
Family £12.00 (2-4 Children)   1 Steam Loco, 1 Diesel

LINESIDE PHOTOGRAPHIC PASSES
£5 Members/Non-Members

The longest 10¼" gauge steam railway in the world using an unique Garratt loco specially built for the line in 1986.

BED & BREAKFAST

Black Lion	01328 820235
Robin Hood	01328 820252

FACILITIES
Souvenir Shop, Light Refreshments in restored Signalbox, Car Park,
Evening Charter train hire (booking essential)

Welsh Highland Railway

Gwynedd

HEADQUARTERS
Gelerts Farm Works, Madoc Street West, Porthmadog, Gwynedd, LL49 9DY.

PRINCIPAL STATIONS
Porthmadog, Pen-y-Mount

HOW TO GET THERE
Road: A487 within town of Porthmadog
Bus: Bws Gwynedd 1, 3, 40, 97
Rail: Porthmadog (adjacent)

☎ Information 01766 513042 Fax 01766 514024

TIMES
Porthmadog   Dep   11.00 12.00 13.30 14.30 15.30 16.30

35 minute round trip including Shed tour.

SERVICE OPERATES
Easter–October
Steam hauled every Sunday/Bank Holidays, all other services Diesel hauled.
Daily July 31st–September 3rd.

1995 SPECIAL EVENTS
Santa Specials   December 9th/10th, 16th/17th.
Mince Pie Specials Christmas – New Year

FARES
Adults £1.25, Child 75p
OAP £1.00, Family £3.00
(2 Adults & 2 Children)

8 Steam Locos, 15 Diesels
1995 LOCOS: *Russell, Gelert*

Locomotive *Russell* is the only survivor of the original Welsh Highland Railway. Given the chance, this railway could become one of the leading Welsh narrow gauge lines with 22 miles of trackbed waiting for them. This line has had a chequered career, and it's not over yet.

FACILITIES
Souvenir Shop, Light Refreshments, Full Meals, Museum, Picnic Site, Car Park.
Wine & Dine on request (minimum no. – 28).

Welshpool & Llanfair Light Railway

Powys

HEADQUARTERS
> The Station, Llanfair Caereinion, Powys, SY21 0SF

PRINCIPAL STATIONS
> Llanfair Caereinion, Castle Caereinion, Welshpool (Raven Square)

HOW TO GET THERE
> Road: A458/490 Junction (Welshpool) Llanfair is 10 miles west of Welshpool on A458
>
> Bus: Cambrian Midland Red
>
> Rail: Welshpool, 1 mile

☎ Information/Enquiries 01938 810441

TIMES

TABLE A

Llanfair Caereinion	Dep	10.30	13.30	16.15
Castle Caereinion	Dep	10.55	13.55	16.40
Welshpool	Arr	11.20	14.20	17.05

All trains call on request at Heniarth, Cyfronydd, Sylfaen

Welshpool	Dep	11.45	14.45	17.15
Castle Caereinion	Dep	12.05	15.05	17.35
Llanfair Caereinion	Arr	12.35	15.35	18.05

TABLE A OPERATES

April 14th, 18th–23rd, 29th/30th. May 6th/7th, 13th/14th, 20th/21st, 27th, 30th/31st. June 1st–4th, 10th/11th, 17th, 20th–22nd, 24th/25th, 27th–29th. July 1st/2nd, 4th–6th, 11th–13th, 15th/16th, 17th–31st. Daily August except 27th/28th. September 1st, 4th–10th, 16th/17th, 23rd/24th.

TABLE B

Llanfair Caereinion	Dep	09.30	10.30	12.00	13.30	14.45	16.15
Castle Caereinion	Dep	09.55	10.55	12.25	13.35	15.10	16.40
Welshpool	Arr	10.20	11.20	12.50	14.20	15.35	17.05

Welshpool	Dep	10.45	12.15	13.45	15.00	16.30	17.15
Castle Caereinion	Dep	11.05	12.35	14.05	15.20	16.50	17.35
Llanfair Caereinion	Arr	11.35	13.05	14.35	15.50	17.20	18.05

TABLE B OPERATES

May 8th, 28th/29th. August 27th/28th.

All trains call on request at Heniarth, Cyfronydd, Sylfaen

Different timetables operate April 15th–17th, June 18th, July 8th/9th, September 2nd/3rd, 30th, October 1st. (See Special Events list).

1995 SPECIAL EVENTS

Free Easter Eggs to
Children   April 15th-17th
Father's Day (Half Fare) June 18th
Friends of *Thomas
the Tank Engine*   July 8th/9th
Narrow Gauge
Steam Gala   September 2nd/3rd
Monster Weekend
(Free rides to children
dressed as monsters)   September 30th/October 1st
Santa Specials   T.B.A.

FARES

Adults £6.50, Child £3.25,
Family £15.00

Length of operating line 8 miles

7 Steam Locos, 2 Diesels

1995 LOCOS
The Countess, No. 85
699.01

BED & BREAKFAST
Goat Hotel 01938 810428

Just a short hop over the Shropshire/Welsh border, this 2'6" gauge line has a mile stretch of 1 in 29 to climb. Locos and rolling stock come from Austria and Antigua amongst other sources.

FACILITIES
Souvenir Shop, Light Refreshments, Disabled Toilet, Picnic Site, Car Park.

Russell getting up steam at the Welsh Highland Railway, Gwynedd

Paul Appleton

West Lancashire Light Railway

Lancs

HEADQUARTERS
Station Road, Hesketh Bank, Nr Preston, Lancs, PR4 6SP

PRINCIPAL STATIONS
Beconsall, Delph

HOW TO GET THERE

Road:	A59 Liverpool–Preston Road, then unclassified from Junction with A565 1.5 miles
Bus:	Ribble/Redline Services 100/102 from Preston
Rail:	Preston or Southport (both approx 8 miles)

☎ Enquiries 01772 815881/218078 Fax 01772 622383

TIMES

Beconsall	Dep 12.30 and every 20 minutes until 17.20
Delph	Dep 12.40 and every 20 minutes until 17.33

SERVICE OPERATES
Easter – Friday, Sunday, Monday.
Then every Sunday until end of October. Bank Holiday Mondays.
Santa Specials: Three Sundays leading up to Christmas.

1995 SPECIAL EVENTS

Gala Day	August 13th
Enthusiasts' Day	October 1st
Santa Specials	December 10th, 17th, 24th

BED & BREAKFAST

Beconsall Hotel	01772 815313
Ruffold Arms	01704 822040
Beaufort Hotel	01704 892655

FARES

Adults £1.00, Child 60p, Family £2.50
All valid for up to 4 return journeys.

Open Sundays 11.30–17.30
& Bank Holiday Fridays and Mondays.

5 Steam Locos, 21 Diesels

1995 LOCOS
Irish Mail, Jonathan, Montalban.

A line that's worth checking out when in the area, preferably early in the day because, considering the length of this ¼ mile line, the ambience of the shed area with loco lighting up can match any big sister railway!

FACILITIES

Souvenir Shop, Picnic Site, Car Park.

Somerset

STANDARD GAUGE

HEADQUARTERS
    The Railway Station, Minehead, Somerset, TA24 5BG
PRINCIPAL STATIONS
    Minehead, Blue Anchor, Watchet, Bishops Lydeard
HOW TO GET THERE
    Road: Bishops Lydeard A358 from Taunton/M5
                  Minehead A39 from Bridgwater/M5
    Bus: Southern National from Taunton to Bishops Lydeard
                  (see Bus Link notes)
    Rail: Taunton, 5 miles to Bishops Lydeard

☎ Talking Timetable 01643 707650, Information 01643 704996, Fax 01643 706349

TIMES
TABLE A (Off Peak)

			D		D
Minehead	Dep	10.15	12.20	14.25	16.45
Dunster	Dep	10.21	12.26	14.31	16.51
Blue Anchor	Dep	10.30	12.32	14.40	17.04
Washford	Dep	10.39	12.40	14.49	17.12
Watchet	Dep	10.47	12.48	14.57	17.20
Doniford Beach (R)	Dep	10.51	12.52	15.01	17.24
Williton	Dep	11.01	12.58	15.08	17.27
Stogumber	Dep	11.14	13.08	15.21	17.37
Crowcombe Heathfield	Dep	11.25	13.15	15.32	17.44
Bishops Lydeard	Arr	11.35	13.24	15.42	17.53

			D		D
Bishops Lydeard	Dep	10.25	12.20	14.40	16.00
Crowcombe Heathfield	Dep	10.35	12.35	14.50	16.15
Stogumber	Dep	10.42	12.44	14.57	16.24
Williton	Dep	10.58	12.57	15.07	16.36
Doniford Beach (R)	Dep	11.01	13.01	15.10	16.40
Watchet	Dep	11.05	13.05	15.14	16.44
Washford	Dep	11.13	13.14	15.22	16.53
Blue Anchor	Dep	11.21	13.22	15.30	17.01
Dunster	Dep	11.27	13.29	15.36	17.06
Minehead	Arr	11.32	13.35	15.41	17.14

NOTES
    D: Diesel Hauled
    (R): Request Stop

TABLE A OPERATES
March 11th/12th, 18th/19th, 25th/26th. April 1st/2nd, 5th/6th, 8th–14th, 21st–23rd, 25th–27th, 29th &30th.
May 2nd–4th, 9th–11th, 13th/14th, 16th–18th, 20th/21st, 23rd–25th.
June 3rd–24th. September 18th–28th, October 3rd–29th (except Mondays & Fridays & 21st/22nd)

TABLE B (Low Peak)

				D
Minehead	Dep 10.15	12.10	14.25	17.15
Dunster	Dep 10.21	12.16	14.31	17.21
Blue Anchor	Dep 10.30	12.25	14.40	17.26
Washford	Dep 10.39	12.34	14.49	17.34
Watchet	Dep 10.47	12.42	14.57	17.42
Doniford Beach (R)	Dep 10.51	12.46	15.01	17.45
Williton	Dep 11.01	12.57	15.08	17.49
Stogumber	Dep 11.14	13.09	15.21	17.59
Crowcombe Heathfield	Dep 11.25	13.20	15.32	18.06
Bishops Lydeard	Arr 11.35	13.30	15.42	18.16

				D
Bishops Lydeard	Dep 10.25	12.20	14.40	16.00
Crowcombe Heathfield	Dep 10.40	12.35	14.50	16.15
Stogumber	Dep 10.49	12.44	14.57	16.24
Williton	Dep 11.01	12.56	15.07	16.36
Doniford Beach (R)	Dep 11.05	13.01	15.10	16.40
Watchet	Dep 11.09	13.05	15.14	16.44
Washford	Dep 11.18	13.14	15.22	16.53
Blue Anchor	Dep 11.26	13.22	15.30	17.01
Dunster	Dep 11.33	13.29	15.36	17.08
Minehead	Arr 11.39	13.35	15.41	17.14

TABLE B OPERATES
April18th–20th,
June 25th–30th,
July 1st–7th, 10th–14th,
September 4th–14th.

NOTES

D: Diesel Hauled
(R): Request Stop

TABLE C (Peak Service)

Minehead	Dep 10.15	12.10	14.00	15.50	17.35
Dunster	Dep 10.21	12.16	14.06	15.56	17.41
Blue Anchor	Dep 10.30	12.25	14.15	16.05	17.50
Washford	Dep 10.39	12.34	14.24	16.14	17.59
Watchet	Dep 10.47	12.42	14.32	16.22	18.07
Doniford Beach (R)	Dep 10.51	12.46	14.36	16.26	18.11
Williton	Dep 11.05	12.57	14.47	16.37	18.22
Stogumber	Dep 11.18	13.10	14.59	16.49	18.35
Crowcombe Heathfield	Dep 11.29	13.21	15.10	17.00	18.46
Bishops Lydeard	Arr 11.39	13.31	15.20	17.10	18.56

Extra Services run
on May 28th–30th,
July 23rd & 30th,
August 6th, 13th,
20th, 27th–29th.

Bishops Lydeard	Dep 10.25	12.20	14.10	16.00	17.45
Crowcombe Heathfield	Dep 10.40	12.35	14.25	16.15	18.00
Stogumber	Dep 10.49	12.44	14.34	16.24	18.09
Williton	Dep 11.05	12.56	14.46	16.36	18.21
Doniford Beach (R)	Dep 11.09	13.01	14.50	16.41	18.26
Watchet	Dep 11.13	13.05	14.54	16.45	18.30
Washford	Dep 11.22	13.14	15.03	16.54	18.39
Blue Anchor	Dep 11.30	13.22	15.11	17.02	18.47
Dunster	Dep 11.37	13.29	15.18	17.09	18.54
Minehead	Arr 11.43	13.35	15.24	17.15	19.00

TABLE C OPERATES
April 15th–17th. May 27th & 31st. June 1st/2nd. July 15th–22nd, 24th–29th & 31st.
August – daily except 6th, 13th, 20th, 27th–29th .
September 1st–3rd.

1995 SPECIAL EVENTS

Mother's Day	March 11th
Spring Gala	May 6th-8th
Model Railway Weekend	June 10th/11th
Teddy Bears' Picnic	June 25th
Wartime Weekend	July 1st/2nd
Friends of *Thomas*	July 8th/9th
Vintage Rally	August 5th/6th
Autumn Steam Weekend	September 16th/17th
Autumn Diesel Gala	September 29th/30th
	October 1st

FARES

Whole Line Returns
Adults £7.70, Child £3.85
OAP £6.20, Family £19.50
(2 Adults & 2 Children)

WINE & DINE

'Quantock Belle' Saturday evenings

The longest line in Britain takes the traveller through the Quantocks and glimpses of the coast before following the coastline to Minehead. The epitomy of an ex-Great Western branch to the seaside, and superb stations too!

Length of operating line 20 miles
(Britain's longest Preserved Railway)

9 Steam Locos, 11 Diesels
1995 LOCOS
S&D No. 88, GWR 4561, 4160, 7828

TAUNTON BUS LINK

Services between Bishops Lydeard and Taunton (BR) are by Southern National, route No. 28A. On WSR Tables A & B, connecting buses depart Taunton BR at 11.20, 15.30. On Table C, buses depart 09.50 (Weds & Sats only) and 11.50. Tel 01823 272033.

DISABLED PASSENGERS

Saloon Carriage 'Lorna Doone' has wheelchair lift, picture windows, and large toilet. Wheelchair passengers travel at child fares. 8 days notice required for party travel in carriage.

FACILITIES

Souvenir Shop, Light Refreshments, Full Meals, On-Train Buffet/Bar, Museums, Picnic Site, Car Parks, Footplate Courses.
PHOTOGRAPHIC PASSES – Members £10.00, Non-Members £15.00

MINEHEAD
Sunfield Private Hotel
Family – run by steam enthusiasts,
4 minutes' walk from WSR station.
B & B £15.00 Evening Meal £7.00
En-Suite Room £19.00.
83 Summerland Avenue,
Minehead, Somerset TA24 5BW.
Tel: (01643) 703565

BED & BREAKFAST

Sunfield Hotel	01643 703565
Tranmere House	01643 702647
Forester Arms	01984 632508

S & D RAILWAY TRUST

The Somerset & Dorset Railway Trust, whose museum is based at Washford Station, have a special train/book launch on June 17th, and an Open Weekend on August 12th/13th.

THE LAST SEA-GOING PADDLE STEAMER IN THE WORLD

HEADQUARTERS
Waverley Steam Navigation Co. Ltd, Gwalia Buildings, Barry Docks, South Glamorgan, CF6 5QR

 01446 720656

Paddlesteamer *Waverley* (which was once railway-owned, hence its inclusion in this book), and sister vessel MV *Balmoral*, carry on the great tradition of Pleasure Steamer trips from ports and piers all around the British Isles.

Sailings from Easter to mid-October, with both full day, afternoon and evening cruises.

1995 PROGRAMME
Includes special trips to connect with the following Steam Railways:

Isle of Man, Swanage, Isle of Wight, Avon Valley, Ravenglass & Eskdale,
West Somerset Railways' Steam Fair & Vintage Transport days, Brecon Mountain Railway
and Romney Hythe & Dymchurch Railway.

Actual sailing times and dates are available in a free programme from the above address.

FACILITIES
Disabled Toilets, Mother & Baby Room, Full Catering, Licensed Bars, Picnic Area
and Souvenir Shop.

Typical fares from £7.95 Adults, £3.95 Children, £5.95 OAP.

Britain's last pleasure steamers will be playing on a World War II theme to commemorate
the great part played by these vessels, and will be welcoming WWII veterans at many ports
around the British Isles.

MUSEUMS AND OTHER SITES OF RAILWAY INTEREST

AIRFIELD LINE – formerly Coventry Steam Railway Centre.
Adjacent to Midlands Air Museum, Rowley Road, Baginton, Coventry. Tel 01455 634373.
Open Easter to October. Sundays 10.00 to 17.00 for static viewing.
Tea and Light Refreshments.

APPLEBY – FRODINGHAM RPS
c/o British Steel, Scunthorpe Works, Scunthorpe, DN16 1BP.
Tel 01724 280280. Society steams on worksite – weekends and midweek by arrangement.

BARNSTAPLE RAILWAY MUSEUM
The Signal Box, Old Town Station, Castle Street, Barnstaple, N.Devon.
Information Centre for the Lynton & Barnstaple Railway Association.
Tel 01271 862930 (eves).

BEAMISH – THE NORTH of ENGLAND OPEN AIR MUSEUM
Beamish, Co. Durham, DH9 ORG. Tel 01207 231811, Fax 01207 290933.
Open Air Museum depicting the North of England at the turn of the century.
Railway locomotives and rolling stock form part of site, also transport collection and 1.5 mile
tramway. Open 10.00–17.00 summer (April to October), last admission 15.00. 10.00–16.00
winter (November to March), last admission 15.00.
BR Newcastle Central & Durham for service buses to Beamish. Connecting bus leaflet and
Special Events leaflet on application to Beamish.

BIRMINGHAM MUSEUM OF SCIENCE & INDUSTRY
Newhall Street, Birmingham 3. Tel 0121 235 1661.
Collection includes railway locomotives and other items of transport interest.
Steam Weekends held in summer. Open daily – phone for details.
Closed Christmas & New Year.
BR Birmingham New Street. Centre Bus route 101.

BIRMINGHAM RAILWAY MUSEUM
Steam Depot, 670 Warwick Road, Tyseley, Birmingham, B11 2HL. Tel 0121 707 4696.
Workshop & maintenance depot for locomotives, mostly ex -GWR.
Open 10.00–17.00 (16.30 or dusk in winter) every day.
BR Tyseley ¼ mile West Midlands Travel Bus route 37.
See Railway Magazines for Special Events.

BRESSINGHAM STEAM MUSEUM
Bressingham, Nr Diss, Norfolk, 1P22 2AB. Tel 01379 687382.
Five miles of railway, both standard and narrow gauges as part of larger Museum of various
Steam attractions. Open 10.00 to 17.30, daily from April to end of September.
In steam Sundays, Thursdays and Bank Holiday Mondays. Santa Specials in December.
BR Diss 2½ miles.

CAERPHILLY RAILWAY SOCIETY
Harold Wilson Industrial Estate, Van Road, Caerphilly, Mid-Glamorgan. Tel 01222 888905.
Viewing every Sunday afternoon. Ring for special operating days.

CAMBRIAN RAILWAYS SOCIETY
Oswald Road, Oswestry, Shropshire. Tel 01691 661648.
Open daily in summer for viewing 10.00–16.00
Telephone for Special operating Steam days.

CLITHEROE STATION MUSEUM
Clitheroe Station, Lancashire.
A new project that hopes to incorporate a railwayana exhibition within the arts centre in the
station buildings.
Tel 01200 25111 ext 5050 for more information.

CONWY VALLEY RAILWAY MUSEUM
The Old Goods Yard, Betws-Y-Coed, Gwynedd, LL24 0AL. Tel 01690 710568.
7¼" gauge steam railway in the grounds, plus 15" gauge tramway. Museum of artefacts
relating to railways of North Wales. Open daily Easter to end of November.
BR Betws-Y-Coed (adjacent)

CORRIS RAILWAY MUSEUM
Corris Station Yard, Corris, Machynlleth, Gwynedd.
Correspondence via A.H Lawson, 165 Gynsill Lane, Anstey, Leics, LE7 7AN.
Displays of unique Corris Railway rolling stock within Corris Railway buildings.2' 3" gauge
railway. Open Weekdays 10.30–17.00 during summer and Bank Holiday weekends.
BR Machynlleth 5 miles.

DARLINGTON RAILWAY CENTRE & MUSEUM
North Road Station, Darlington, Co. Durham, DL3 6ST. Tel 01325 460532.
This restored 1842 station of the historic Stockton & Darlington Railway houses relics
relating to S & DR including *Locomotion* of 1825.
Open daily 09.30–17.00 except Christmas and New Year holidays (last admission 16.30).
BR Darlington North Road (adjacent).

DOWNPATRICK STEAM RAILWAY
Market Street, Downpatrick BT30 6LZ. Tel 01396 616 5779.
Steam weekends and Bank Holidays.

ERIDGE RAILWAY CENTRE.
Eridge Station, Nr Crowborough, East Sussex.
Site open weekends. Society aim to re-open Eridge to Tunbridge Wells section.
BR Eridge (adjacent).

FFESTINIOG RAILWAY MUSEUM
At Harbour Station, Ffestiniog Railway, Porthmadog, Gwynedd.
Open during railway operating hours (see Main Railways section), the museum features
FR history, and contains original locomotive *Princess*.
BR & FR Porthmadog.

FOYLE VALLEY RAILWAY CENTRE
Foyle Road Station, Derry City BT48 6SQ. Tel 01504 265234.
Collection of County Donegal Railway items, both steam and railcar.
Open – Tuesdays to Saturdays and public holidays 10.00–17.00. Sundays April to September.
NIR Londonderry ½ mile.

GLASGOW MUSEUM OF TRANSPORT
Kelvin Hall, Glasgow, G3 8DP. Tel 0141 357 3929.
Exhibits representing the major Scottish Railways including ex-Glasgow tramcars, steam
locomotives and subway gallery.
Open daily 10.00–17.00. Sundays 14.00 to 17.00. Closed Christmas & New Years Days.
Glasgow Subway – Kelvin Hall

GLENFINNAN STATION MUSEUM
Glenfinnan Station, Glenfinnan, Scotland.
Exhibits relating to West Highland line. No other details available.
BR Glenfinnan (adjacent).

GREAT CENTRAL (Nottingham)
Mere Way, Ruddington, Nottingham NG11 6NX. Tel 01602 405705.
Transport Heritage centre on site of future Great Central Railway
extension towards Nottingham. Open Sundays and Bank Holidays.

GREAT WESTERN RAILWAY MUSEUM
Farringdon Road, Swindon, Wiltshire, SN1 5BJ . Tel 01793 70752.
Situated in the centre of the Railway Village Conservation Area, the museum is entirely
devoted to relics of the GWR. Locomotives include *King George V* and *North Star*. Open
Monday to Saturday 10.00–17.00. Sundays 14.00–17.00. Closed Good Friday, Christmas Day
and Boxing Day.
BR Swindon, ¼ mile.

GREAT WESTERN RAILWAY MUSEUM (COLEFORD)
Coleford Main Car Park, Coleford, Gloucestershire. Tel 01594 833569.
Full sized relics with 7¼" gauge miniature railway, housed in 1883 GWR buildings.
Variable opening hours. Tel for details.
BR Lydney 7 miles – Red & White Bus Service No.31.

HIGHLAND RAILWAY MUSEUM
ScotRail Station, Nairn, Scotland.
Displaying relics of both Highland Railway and national origin.
Open June to September 10.00 to 17.00. Closed Tuesdays and Fridays.
BR Nairn (adjacent).

IRCHESTER NARROW GAUGE RAILWAY MUSEUM
Irchester Country Park, Irchester, Wellingborough, Northamptonshire.
A working museum depicting the former narrow gauge Industrial railways of the East
Midlands and Northamptonshire – famed for their Ironstone lines.
Open every Sunday 10.00–18.00 in summer. 10.00–17.00 winter, and
Bank Holiday Mondays.
BR Wellingborough, 2½ miles.

ISLE OF MAN RAILWAY MUSEUM

Strand Road, Port Erin, Isle of Man. Tel 01624 833432/663366.
Contains exhibits relating to the Isle of Man Railways including the first locomotive
Sutherland (1873) and the royal coach.
Open early April to end of October 10.00 to 16.00
Isle of Man Steam Railway – Port Erin Station.

LEGBOURNE RAILWAY MUSEUM

The Old Station, Legbourne, Louth, Lincolnshire. Tel 01507 603116.
Mike Legges' collection of Lincolnshire railway artefacts in the restored Great Northern
Railway Station and Signal Box.
Open Easter to end of September. 10.30–17.00. Not Mondays except Bank Holidays.

LLECHWEDD SLATE CAVERNS

Blaenau Ffestiniog, Gwynedd, LL41 3NB. Tel 01766 830306.
Travel on an underground incline railway to explore the famous slate mines.
Winding gear demonstrations. Victorian village built around mine.
BR & FR Blaenau Ffestiniog, 1 mile.

LONDON TRANSPORT MUSEUM

Covent Garden, London, WC2E 7BB. Tel 0171 379 6344.
Re-developed in December 1993, the museum tells the story of London's famous transport
system and its effect on the growth of London and peoples lives. Underground rolling stock,
buses, models and trams.
Open daily 10.00–18.00, last admission 17.15. Closed December 24th–26th.
Underground: Covent Garden.

MANX ELECTRIC RAILWAY MUSEUM

Ramsey Station, Isle of Man. Tel 01624 663366 for opening times.
Collection of vehicles, equipment and photographs from the M.E.R and former
Ramsey Pier Railway.
MER Ramsey Station.

MID NORFOLK RAILWAY SOCIETY

County School Station, North Elmham, Norfolk, NR20 5LE.
Fledgling society restoring station site with ultimate aim to connect track to Dereham.
400 yard track with steam and diesel operating days.

MID SUFFOLK LIGHT RAILWAY MUSEUM
Brockford Station, off A140 Ipswich - Norwich road, Suffolk.
Artefacts relating to the Mid Suffolk Light Railway.
Open every Sunday & Bank Holiday from Easter to end of September.

MONKWEARMOUTH STATION MUSEUM
North Bridge Street, Sunderland, Tyne & Wear, SR5 1AP. Tel 0191 567 7075.
This former station on the ECML displays rolling stock and local transport historical items.
Opening times Tuesdays to Fridays 10.00 to 17.00, Saturdays 10.00 to 17.30,
Sundays 14.00 to 17.00, Bank Holiday Mondays 10.00 to 16.30
BR Sunderland ½ mile.

MUSEUM OF ARMY TRANSPORT
Flemingate, Beverley, North Humberside, HU17 0NG. Tel. 01482 860445.
Britain's only Army Railway Museum includes the former collection of the Longmoor
Military Railway and many Army railway locomotives from the Royal Corps of Transport
collection. Also Army road, sea and air exhibits.
Open daily 10.00–17.00. Closed December 24th–26th.
BR Beverley, ¼ mile.

MUSEUM OF SCIENCE & INDUSTRY (MANCHESTER)
Liverpool Road Station, Castlefield, Manchester, M3 4JP. Tel 0161 832 2244.
At the oldest passenger railway station in the world, exhibits of locomotives and rolling stock
include the *Planet* replica.
Open daily 10.00–17.00. Closed December 23rd–25th.
BR Deansgate ¼ mile.

NARROW GAUGE RAILWAY MUSEUM
Tywyn Station, Talyllyn Railway, Tywyn, Gwynedd, LL36 9EY.
A collection of items from narrow gauge railways across Britain, from rolling stock
and locomotives to tickets.
Open daily from Easter to the end of October.
BR & TR: Tywyn.

NATIONAL RAILWAY MUSEUM
Leeman Road, York, YO2 4XJ. Tel 01904 621261.
Now covering twice its original area, the National Collection encompasses both steam and
modern locomotives, carriages, rolling stock with ancillary displays showing the influence of
the railway on the lives of the British people.
Open Mondays to Saturdays 10.00–18.00, Sundays 11.00–18.00, last admission 17.00.
BR York 400 yards.

NORTHANTS IRONSTONE RAILWAY TRUST
Hunsbury Hill Country Park, West Hunsbury, Northampton. Tel 01604 811130.
Another site that covers the interest shown in Northamptonshires Ironstone lines.
Open Easter to Christmas Eve Weekends.

NORTH WOOLWICH STATION MUSEUM
Pier Road, North Woolwich, London, E16 2JJ. Tel 0171 474 7244.
Museum of the Great Eastern Railway Society housed in and around the 1854 station
building. Some locomotives in steam first Sundays in summer months.
Open Monday to Wednesday & Saturday 10.00–17.00. Sundays & Bank Holidays
14.00–17.00. Closed Thursday & Friday.
BR North Woolwich (adjacent). Woolwich Ferry (adjacent).

ONGAR RAILWAY PRESERVATION SOCIETY (Epping Forest Railway)
Information Tel 01992 523749.
Society aims to restore services, including steam, to the Epping-Ongar section, recently
closed by London Underground – part of the former Great Eastern Railway, Have restored
signal box at North Weald and are currently obtaining rolling stock.

OXENHOPE RAILWAY MUSEUM
Oxenhope Station Yard, Oxenhope, West Yorkshire.
Situated at the southern terminus of the Keighley & Worth Valley Railway,
(see Main Railways section). Home to the railway's dining car fleet – this impressive building
provides accommodation to many gems of the KWVR collection, featuring locomotives,
coaches and railway memorabilia.
KWVR Oxenhope.

PENRHYN CASTLE INDUSTRIAL RAILWAY MUSEUM
Penrhyn, Nr Bangor, Gwynedd, North Wales. Tel 01248 53084.
Exhibits include ex-Penrhyn Railway locomotives and rolling stock and Dinorwic Quarry
locomotive *Fire Queen* of 1848.
Open daily beginning of April to end of November, 12.00–17.00. Closed Tuesdays.
BR Bangor 3 miles.

PLYM VALLEY RAILWAY
Marsh Mills Station, Plymouth, Devon, PL7 4NL.
Various items of railway interest on site, with ultimate intention to restore steam service.
Site open weekends. Write for further details.
BR Plymouth 3 miles.

RAILWORLD

Oundle Road, Peterborough, Cambridgeshire PE2 9NR. Tel 01733 344240.
Situated at the eastern end of the Nene Valley Railway (see Main Railways section),
exhibitions include 'Rail and the environment', a look at global rail travel, a local display for
Peterborough's 150 railway years in 1995, steam locos and rolling stock from many countries.
Open daily 11.00–16.00 (Mon–Fri only Nov.–Feb.). Closed Christmas/New Year.

RUSHDEN TRANSPORT MUSEUM

Old Station, Rectory Road, Rushden, Northants. Tel 01933 318988.
Exhibits include railway rolling stock in platform road, and small relics museum.
Other items of transport interest on site. Society aim to restore
steam service.
BR Wellingborough 5 miles.

SCIENCE MUSEUM

Exhibition Road, London SW7 2DD. Tel 0171 938 8000.
Whilst the bulk of the National collection is at York, various railway locomotives
feature as part of a broader transport theme in London.
Open daily 10.00–18.00 (11.00 Sundays)
Underground: South Kensington 350 yards.

SCOTTISH INDUSTRIAL RAILWAY CENTRE

Minnevey Colliery, Burnton, Dalmellington, Ayrshire. Tel 01929 313579.
Representing Scottish interests in the Industrial field, the railway locomotives and rolling
stock cover standard and narrow gauge. (See Ayrshire Railway in Main Railways section).
Open 11.00–16.00 Saturdays from June to end of September. Tel for steaming dates.
(No public transport access)

SOMERSET & DORSET RAILWAY TRUST

Washford Station, Washford, Somerset. Tel 01984 40869.
Includes museum of Somerset & Dorset Railway relics with ex-Midford signal cabin.
Rolling stock on display. Special events planned see West Somerset Railway entry.
Part of West Somerset Railway's Washford Station (See Main Railways section).
Open 11.00–17.00 weekends and Bank Holidays from Easter to end of October, and daily late
July to end of October.
WSR Washford (adjacent).

SOUTHALL RAILWAY CENTRE
Southall, Middlesex UB2 4PL. Tel 0181 574 1529.
Centre being established by the G.W.R. Preservation Group.
Steam and diesel exhibits, both with 'Driver Experience sessions'.
Tel for opening times.

SOUTHWOLD MUSEUM
Bartholomew Green, Southwold, Suffolk.
A collection of photographs, paperwork and relics relating to the
Southwold Railway – an early closure of 1929, as part of town museum.
Open daily 14.30–16.30 from Spring Bank Holiday to end of September, also Easter
BR Halesworth 9 miles. Easter Counties Buses – various routes.

SOUTH YORKSHIRE RAILWAY
Barrow Road Sidings, Meadowhall, Sheffield. Tel 0114 242440.
Only members currently allowed on site.
Some open days planned – see Railway press for details.

STEPHENSON RAILWAY MUSEUM
North Tyneside Steam Railway.
Middle Engine Lane, West Chirton, North Shields, NE29 8DX. Tel 0191 262 2627.
Open weekends and Bank Holidays only – Easter to end of October.

TELFORD HORSEHAY STEAM TRUST
Old Locomotive Shed, Horsehay, Telford, Shropshire. Tel 01952 503880.
Ex-GWR and other stock at Horsehay. Tel for further information.
BR Telford Central 2½ miles.

TENTERDEN MUSEUM
Station Road, Tenterden, Kent. Tel 01580 763350/764310.
Many artefacts relating to the light railways of Colonel Stephens and the
Kent & East Sussex Railway in particular.
Open Daily April to end of October 14.00–16.45, August 11.00–16.45. Closed Fridays.
At town end of Tenterden Station approach road (see Main Railway section).
K&ESR Tenterden 200 yards, BR Headcorn 9 miles, Appledore 8 miles.

TIMOTHY HACKWORTH RAILWAY MUSEUM
Soho Cottages, Shildon, Co. Durham DL4 2QX. Tel 01388 777999.
The home and workplace of Timothy Hackworth, a steam locomotive pioneer.
Replica of *Sanspareil* that competed in the Rainhill trials of 1829.
Open Wednesdays to Saturdays 10.00–17.00 Easter to last Sunday in October.
BR Shildon ¼ mile.

TIVERTON MUSEUM
St. Andrews Street, Tiverton, Devon. Tel 01884 256295.
Displaying ex - GWR 0-4-2T locomotive 1442 of 1935, this town museum also
displays relics of Great Western Canal interest.
Open daily except Sundays and late December to end of January, 10.30–16.30.
BR Tiverton Parkway 6 miles. Tiverton & District Buses – various routes.

ULSTER FOLK AND TRANSPORT MUSEUM
Cultra Manor, Holywood, Co. Down, Northern Ireland. Tel 01232 428428.
8 miles from Belfast, exhibits include the award winning 'Irish Railway Collection'
in new purpose built gallery. Road, Rail, sea and air travel in Ireland.
Open daily Easter to September 11.00–17.00.
NIR Cultra (short walk).

VINTAGE CARRIAGE TRUST RAILWAY CARRIAGE MUSEUM
Ingrow Station, Keighley, West Yorkshire. Tel 01535 680425/646472.
Museum contains a unique collection of historic railway carriages, with access to restored
vehicles. Also next to home of *Bahamas* society, and part of Ingrow Railway Centre.
Open weekends throughout the year. Daily Bank Holiday weeks and mid-June to end of
August, 11.30–17.00.
BR Keighley 1½ miles. KWVR Ingrow/West station (adjacent) (see Main Railways section).

WINCHCOMBE RAILWAY MUSEUM
23 Gloucester Street, Winchcombe, Gloucestershire. Tel 01242 620641.
Museum containing a mass of railwayana from the collection of Tim Petchey.
The garden is well known for its range of railway cast iron notices.
Combine with trip to Gloucestershire & Warwickshire Railway (see Main Railways section).
13.30–18.00 Easter to end of October weekends, daily throughout August.
BR Cheltenham Spa 9 miles. GWR Winchcombe.

WOLFERTON STATION MUSEUM

Wolferton Station, Wolferton, Nr. Kings Lynn, Norfolk PE31 6HA. Tel 01485 540674.
Former royal station on the Sandringham Estate, used until 1966.
See the royal retiring rooms built for King Edward VII and Queen Alexandra in 1898.
Items and furniture from royal trains, Queen Victoria's travelling bed, GER coach.
Open daily Easter to September – Weekdays 11.00–17.30, Saturdays 10.30–16.30,
Sundays 13.00–17.00
BR Kings Lynn 7½ miles. Eastern Counties Bus 410 (1 mile).

WORKSHOPS TO THE WORLD - ELSECAR PROJECT

Elsecar Workshops, Wath Road, Elsecar, Barnsley, South Yorkshire S74 8HJ.
Tel 01226 740203. Fax 01226 350239.
On the site of the Elsecar Ironworks, many different attractions and recreations of the
Industrial age are on show including workshops, real ale brewery, beam engine and the
Fitzwilliam Railway. Built to serve several colliery lines, the 45 minute journey is
hauled by 0–6–0 ST Avonside of 1917/23 now named *Earl Fitzwilliam*.
Open daily 09.00–17.00 except December 25th–26th.
BR Elsecar, follow signs by foot to 'Elsecar Heritage'.

WYLAM RAILWAY MUSEUM

Falcon Centre, Falcon Wylam, Northumberland.
The birthplace of 'Puffing Billy', this museum tells the story of Wylam's place in
early railway history.
Open Tuesdays/Thursdays 14.00–19.30, Saturdays 09.00–Noon.
BR Wylam ¼ mile.

Standard gauge tramway engine *Sir Vincent*, built by Aveling & Porter in 1917. Photographed at the Nene Valley Railway and now at Hunsbury Hill, Northampton

Eric Sawford

LMS No. 6233 *Duchess of Sutherland* stands outside the shed at Bressingham Steam Museum, Norfolk, in August 1994

Eric Sawford

OTHER NARROW AND MINIATURE GAUGED RAILWAYS

ABBEY LIGHT RAILWAY
Kirkstall Abbey, Leeds, West Yorkshire.
2' gauge line runs from Kirkstall Abbey to Bridge Road.
Normally diesel haulage. Bridge Road Workshops open for viewing.

AUDLEY END MINIATURE RAILWAY
Audley End, Saffron Walden, Essex.
10 ¼" gauge main track, plus other gauges represented.
Operates weekends in summer and daily Easter and school holidays.

BAMBRIDGE RAILWAY
Bambridge Park Garden Centre, Eastleigh, Hampshire.
8¼ " gauge – 180 yards.

BARLEYLANDS RAILWAY
Barleylands Farm Museum, Billericay, Essex.
7¼ " gauge – 800 yards.

BEALE LIGHT RAILWAY
Beale Bird Park, Pangbourne, Berkshire.
7¼" gauge – 900 yards.
Operates March to September.

BEER HEIGHTS LIGHT RAILWAY
Beer, Nr Seaton, Devon.
Part of Peco, model railway accessory manufacturers 'Pecorama' complex.
7¼ " gauge. 10.00–17.30 weekdays. Saturdays 10.00–13.00.
Permanent model railway exhibition and shop.

BETWS-Y-COED MINIATURE RAILWAY
Betws-y-Coed, Gwynedd.
7¼ " gauge adjacent to Conwy Valley Railway Museum.

BICKINGTON STEAM RAILWAY
Trago Mills, Bickington, Newton Abbot, Devon.
10¼ " gauge.
11.00–17.00 Easter to October, some winter weekends.

BICTON WOODLAND RAILWAY
Bicton Gardens, Budleigh Salterton, Devon.
18" gauge. 1 mile. Loco 0–4–0T *Woolwich* from Woolwich Arsenal.

BROOKSIDE GARDEN CENTRE RAILWAY
Macclesfield Road, Poynton, Cheshire.
7¼ " gauge. Railwayana museum. Integrated signalling system. Tel 01625 872919.
April – September Wednesdays/Sundays,
July & August – Tuesday, Wednesday, Thursday, Sunday, 11.30–17.00.

COATE PARK RAILWAY
Coate Water Park, Swindon, Wiltshire.
dual gauged railway 5" & 7¼ ".
Sundays Easter to October 14.00–17.00.

CROXTETH PARK RAILWAY
Croxteth Hall Estate, Liverpool, Merseyside.
7¼" gauge.
Easter to end of October. Steam on selected Sundays.

EASTBOURNE MINIATURE STEAM RAILWAY
Lottbridge Drive, Eastbourne, Sussex.
7¼ " gauge – 100 yards.

EASTLEIGH LAKESIDE RAILWAY
Fleming Park, Eastleigh, Hants.
7¼" gauge. Operates Sunday afternoons in season.

EAST HERTS MINIATURE RAILWAY
Van Hage's Garden Centre, Great Amwell, Hertfordshire.
7¼ " gauge.

ECHILLS WOOD RAILWAY
Stoneleigh, Kenilworth, Warwickshire.
7¼ " gauge at Royal Agricultural Showground.
Operates at major showground events.

EXMOOR STEAM CENTRE
Cape of Good Hope Farm, Bratton Fleming, N. Devon.
12¼ " gauge. ¾ mile circuit, trains every 20 minutes. Tel 01598 710711.
Open weekends and holidays throughout the year. Daily in High Season.
Shop/Restaurant Complex. Steam Gala Weekend – first weekend in May.

FERRY MEADOWS RAILWAY
Nene Park, Peterborough, Cambridgeshire.
10¼ " gauge.

GARTELL LIGHT RAILWAY
Common Lane, Yenston, Nr Templecombe, Somerset.
Operates special days between April and September.
Tel 01963 70752. Santa Specials in December.

GREAT COCKROW RAILWAY
Hardwick Lane, Lyne, Nr Chertsey, Surrey.
7¼ " gauge fully signalled and track-circuited. Approx 1 mile.
Operates Sundays 14.30–17.30 May to mid-October.

GREAT TORRINGTON RAILWAY
Mill Lodge, Town Mills, Torrington, Devon.
7¼" gauge – 800 yards.

GREAT WHIPSNADE RAILWAY
Whipsnade Wild Animal Park, Dunstable Bedfordshire.
Daily Easter to September, Saturdays/Sundays March to October.
Direct buses from Hemel Hempstead BR.

HAIGH HALL RAILWAY
Haigh Hall Country Park, Wigan, Lancs.
15" gauge.

HALTON MINIATURE RAILWAY
Town Park, Palacefields, Runcorn, Cheshire.
7¼ " gauge – 1½ miles.
Sundays and Bank Holidays all year round, 13.00–17.00.

HOLLYCOMBE MINIATURE RAILWAY
Hollycombe House, Liphook, Hants.
7¼ " gauge.
Part of a larger steam museum complex.

KERRS MINIATURE RAILWAY
West Links, Arbroath, Scotland.
10¼ " gauge – 400 yards.
Weekends Easter to September. Daily July and early August.

KEW BRIDGE MINIATURE RAILWAY
Green Dragon Lane, Brentford, Middlesex.
Miniature railway operates twice a month March to November,
as part of steam museum. Tel 0181 568 4757.

KNEBWORTH MINIATURE RAILWAY
Knebworth House, Nr Stevenage, Herts.
10¼ " gauge – 600 yards.
Operates weekends and Bank Holidays Easter to September
and Tuesdays to Fridays during school holidays.

LAKESHORE RAILROAD
South Marine Park, South Shields, Tyne & Wear.
9½ " gauge – 500 yards, features American locos.
Weekends Easter to October and daily June to August.

LAKESIDE MINIATURE RAILWAY
Marine Lake, Southport, Merseyside.
15" gauge – 1,300 yards.

LAPPA VALLEY RAILWAY
Newlyn East, Newquay, Cornwall.
15" gauge – 2 miles return. Also 7¼" gauge line.
Daily Easter to September 10.30–17.30.

LEASOWES PARK MINIATURE RAILWAY
Mucklow Hill, Halesowen, West Midlands.
7¼ "gauge.

LIGHTWATER VALLEY RAILWAY
North Stainley, Ripon, N. Yorkshire.
15" gauge – 1 mile.
Operating days – tel 01765 635321/635359.

LITTLE HEREFORD LIGHT RAILWAY
Haynall farm, Little Hereford, Nr Ludlow.
7¼ " gauge – 400 yards.

LONDON TOY & MODEL MUSEUM
21/23 Craven Hill, London W2.
7¼ " gauge – 90 yards.

LONGLEAT RAILWAY
Longleat, Warminster, Wilts.
15" gauge, 1¼ miles in Stately Home grounds.
Daily Easter to end of October.

MANOR MINIATURE RAILWAY
Manor Park, Glossop, Derbyshire.
7¼ " gauge – ½ mile. Sundays and Bank Holidays, Saturdays in summer.

MIZENS RAILWAY
Mizens Farm, Woking, Surrey.
7¼ " gauge. Approx 1 mile. First and last Sunday of the month.
14.00–17.00 Easter to September.

MOORS VALLEY RAILWAY
Moors Valley Country Park, Ashley Heath, Dorset.
7¼ " gauge. 9 steam locos. Weekends throughout the year.
Easter week and daily Whitsun to mid-September.

MYDDLEWOOD RAILWAY
Myddlewood, Buschurch, Salop.
7¼ " gauge.

NARROWER GAUGE RAILWAY
Eirias Park, Colwyn Bay, Clwyd.
10¼ " gauge – 400 yards.

NEWBY HALL MINIATURE RAILWAY
Newby Hall, Ripon, N. Yorkshire.
10¼ " gauge.

NORTH GLOUCESTER RAILWAY
Toddington Station, Gloucestershire.
2' gauge line. Sundays in summer season.

NORTON ASH RAILWAY
Norton Ash Nursery, Teynham, Faversham, Kent.
9" gauge – 200 yards.

PAPPLEWICK MINIATURE RAILWAY
Papplewick Pumping Station Museum, Ravenshead, Notts.
7¼" gauge – 1,000 ft long.

PENTNEY PARK RAILWAY
Pentney Park Caravan Site, Nr Swaffham, Norfolk.
7¼ " gauge – ¾ mile. Saturday evenings,
Sunday afternoons during summer.

POLYTECHNIC STADIUM RAILWAY
Hartington Road, Chiswick, London W4.
10¼ " gauge – 750 yards.

POOL PARK MINIATURE RAILWAY
Pool Park, Poole, Dorset.
10¼ " gauge – 900 yards.

QUEEN MARY'S RAILWAY
Queen Mary's Hospital for Sick Children, Carshalton, Surrey.
10¼ " gauge – ½ mile.
Open Sunday afternoons 14.30–16.30 May to September.

RHIW VALLEY RAILWAY
Lower House Farm , Manafon, Welshpool, Powys.
15" gauge – 1¼ miles.
Open by appointment only.

RODE WOODLAND RAILWAY
Tropical Bird Gardens, Rode, Nr Bath, Somerset.
7¼ " gauge.
Daily except Dec. 25th. 13.00–18.30 (dusk in winter).

RHYL MINIATURE RAILWAY
Marine Lake, Rhyl, Clwyd.
15" gauge.

RUISLIP LIDO RAILWAY
Reservoir Road, Ruislip, Middlesex.
12" gauge – 1½ miles.
Sundays throughout the year and daily Easter to October
except Tuesdays & Thursdays in April, May, September & October.

RUSWARP MINIATURE RAILWAY
The Carrs, Ruswarp, Nr Whitby, N.Yorkshire.
7¼ " gauge – 700 yards.

SANDTOFT LIGHT RAILWAY
Sandtoft Transport Centre, Nr Doncaster, Yorkshire.
7¼ " gauge – 400 yards.
Part of transport complex including trolleybus route.

SAUNDERSFOOT STEAM RAILWAY
Stepaside, Saundersfoot, Dyfed.
15" gauge – 400 yards.

One of the few steam lines that can boast a full 'genuine' Pullman dining facility is the Bluebell Railway. Pullman Parlour Third Car No. 64 stands at Sheffield Park in readiness for its evening trip

Colin Tyson

The most unusual of locomotives was restored in 1988 at the Middleton Railway. Ex-LNER 'Sentinel' No. 54 shunts at Moor Road during the railway's 30th anniversary celebrations in 1990

Paul Appleton

SHIBDEN PARK RAILWAY
Shibden Park, Halifax, W. Yorkshire.
10¼ " gauge.

SOMERLEYTON HALL MINIATURE RAILWAY
Nr Lowestoft, Suffolk.
7¼ " gauge – ¼ mile.
Open 14.00–18.00 April to October Sundays,
Thursdays & Bank Holiday Mondays.
Also Tuesdays & Wednesdays in July & August.

STRATHAVEN MINIATURE RAILWAY
George Allen Park, Strathaven, Lanarkshire.
Dual 5" & 7¼ " gauge railway – 1,200' length.
Saturdays & Sundays 13.00–17.00 from Easter to end of September.

SWANLEY NEW BARN RAILWAY
New Barn Park, Swanley, Kent.
7¼ " gauge – 900 yards.

THAMES DITTON MINIATURE RAILWAY
Claygate Lane, Thames Ditton, Surrey.
7¼ " gauge – ½ mile.
First Sunday of each month. Bank Holiday Sundays & Mondays.
Easter to October 14.00–17.30.

THORNES PARK RAILWAY
Thornes Park, Horbury Road, Wakefield, West Yorkshire.
7¼ " gauge – 800 yards.

TWYFORD COUNTRY CENTRE
Twyford Farm, Evesham, Worcestershire.
7¼ " gauge – 200 yards.

VANSTONE RAILWAY
Vanstone Park Garden, Hitchin Road, Codicote,, Herts.
10¼" gauge – 520 yards.
Weekend & Bank Holidays 11.00–17.00.
Tel 01438 820412.

VOBSTER LIGHT RAILWAY
Holwell Farm, Wells, Somerset.
2' gauge.
Occasional running days.

VICTORIA PARK RAILWAY
Royal Victoria Country park, Netley, Southampton, Hants.
10¼ " gauge – ¾ mile.
Every weeekend and daily during school holidays.

WALSALL ARBORETUM RAILWAY
Broadway North, Walsall, West Midlands.
7¼ " gauge – 1¼ miles.
Open every Sunday & Bank Holidays from 13.00 from Easter to October.

WATFORD MINIATURE RAILWAY
Cassiobury Park, Watford, Herts.
10¼ " gauge – 400 yards.

WELLINGTON COUNTRY PARK STEAM RAILWAY
Wellington Country Park, Heckfield, Nr Basingstoke, Hants.
7¼ " gauge.

WESTON PARK RAILWAY
Shifnal, Salop.
7¼ " gauge – 1¼ miles.
Open weekends & Bank Holidays Easter to end of September &
most weekends in June, July & August.

WILLEN MINIATURE RAILWAY
Willen Lakeside Park, Milton Keynes, Buckinghamshire.
7¼ " gauge – ½ mile.
Open weekends throughout the year. Daily in summer.

WILD BOAR RAILWAY
Metal Bridge, Nr Ferryhill, Co. Durham.
7¼ " gauge – 180 yards.

LATE ENTRY
NICKELODEON LINE
Ashorne Hall Nickelodeon, Nr Warwick.
12¼" gauge – 1 mile.
Open every Sunday from April 9th–November 5th
plus Bank Holidays and Saturdays in July & August. 13.30–17.30.
Closed June 4th/11th. Signed from Junction 13/14, M40.

FURTHER INFORMATION

If you wish to keep abreast of current news and events on railways listed in this book, the following publications are available from all good newsagents.

RAILWAY MAGAZINE
Monthly £2.10
Published by IPC Magazines Ltd, Kings Reach Tower,
Stamford Street, London SE1 9LS.

RAILWAY WORLD
Monthly £1.90
Published by Ian Allan Ltd, Coombelands House,
Addlestone, Weybridge, Surrey KH15 1HY.

STEAM CLASSIC
Monthly £1.95
Published by Ebony Publishing,
Heathlands Industrial Estate, Heathlands Road,
Liskeard, Cornwall PL14 4DH.

STEAM RAILWAY
Monthly £2.10
Published by Emap Apex Publications,
Apex House, Oundle Road, Peterborough
Cambs PE2 9NP.

STEAM RAILWAY NEWS
Weekly £0.70
Published by Lacashire Publications Ltd,
Martland Mill, Martland Mill Lane,
Wigan WN5 0LX.

Several steam railways hold Vintage Steam Traction Engine events at their sites. For more information see

OLD GLORY
Monthly £2.30
Published by CMS Publishing,
31 Scotgate, Stamford, Lincolnshire, PE9 2YQ.